PRAISE FOR

So You Got Into Medical School . . .

"If only I had been given a copy of Dr. Paull's book before I entered medical school, it would have saved me so much heartache and time—from MCATs through residency selection and even board certification. Not having this book, I felt like others kept a secret they didn't want me to know. Well, thanks to Dan Paull, the secret is out."

—*Jerrold S. Polansky, MD*

"This book, written in a readable and conversational style, speaks to my own experience in medical school. Medical students will find themselves nodding along with the true (and often very funny) stories and glean many helpful tips to make the most of an expensive and arduous four-year journey. There is no other book on the market like it."

—*Max Falkoff, MD*

"This easy-to-read book is well done, with good concepts and practical information. The section on efficiency and sleep is particularly good—a subject I'm always trying to drive home with my students (and patients). I'll have to make it required reading."

—*Andrew Lehmann, MD*

So You Got into Medical School... Now What?

A Guide to Preparing for the Next Four Years

DANIEL R. PAULL, MD

STIRTON-HUGHES PUBLISHERS

Stirton-Hughes Publishers
580 Craig Drive #8-123
Perrysburg, OH 43551
www.soyougotintomedicalschool.com

Ordering Information
Quantity sales. Special discounts are available on quantity purchases by corporations, associations, and others. For details, contact the "Special Sales Department" at the address above.

Printed in the United States of America

First Edition

20 19 18 17 16 15   10 9 8 7 6 5 4 3 2 1

ISBN: 978-0-9909400-4-3

Cover design illustration by Dyani Loo

Cover design by Kuo Design

Interior design by Graffolio

Copyediting by PeopleSpeak

To my grandparents,
Sidney and Estelle Fruchtman—
I wouldn't be where I am without you

Also special thanks to Dyani Loo

Contents

Introduction vii

1   Conceptual Learning and Detail Worrying 1

2   Study Efficiency 19

3   Diminishing Returns 49

4   Avoiding Study Anxiety 65

5   Studying for the USMLE Step 1: 91
     End of the Second Year

6   Transition to the Third Year 101

7   Clerkships 109

8   Studying for the USMLE Step 2 CK 139

9   The USMLE Step 2 CS 149

10   The Fourth Year in a Nutshell 157

11   The Away Rotation 179

12   The Residency Interview 201

     Conclusion 219

     Index 221

     About the Author 229

Introduction

Congratulations on getting into medical school. With many applicants taking time off to résumé-build and the average accepted MCAT (Medical College Admission Test) score rising yearly, the applicant pool for entrance is increasingly competitive. Many say the hardest part of medical school is getting in. Reflecting back on my own medical school career, I can say with confidence that getting in was the hard part. So again, congratulations on being one of the select few. Now let out a sigh of relief. All those years of hard work and extracurricular activities have paid off.

Starting medical school is nerve-racking. Rumor is, medical students study from sunup to sundown, with no time to enjoy themselves. Mentally preparing for this type of life is a thankless hardship. The fact is, these rumors are false. As with most meaningful endeavors, the intensity of medical school occurs in cycles. Sometimes as a medical student you'll have to study most of the day, but now and then you'll have free time! You won't have to give up all your hobbies if you work intelligently and efficiently. The point of this book is to help you learn how to best manage your time in medical school. I almost always had time to do what I desired, and most weekends I was able to enjoy myself. I never had to pull an all-nighter, and seldom did I even have to study past 10:00 p.m. My goal was always to do well in school while enduring as little stress as possible.

Sadly, this was not the case for a lot of my classmates, who all too often worked inefficiently and as a result became stressed, trading free time for anxiety. I learned how to avoid this trap through trial and error but often wished someone had told me what medical school was *really* going to be like. This guidebook is designed to help the student who is now in the position I once found myself in—without a guide. It is meant to help the novice medical student generate a game plan to be efficient, do well in school, and incur minimal stress.

The chapters concerning the first and second years of medical school are meant to be read the summer before you start school, while the remaining chapters can be read at your leisure, sometime before the start of the third year. Each chapter starts with a vignette taken from my life—from in-class studying to enduring the daily grind of a hard rotation. Here you will glimpse the sights, sounds, and feelings of a medical student, and each vignette is followed by instruction about how, with efficiency, intelligence, and minimal stress, to tackle medical school. Remember this: medical school isn't as bad as everyone says it is as long as you avoid making the mistakes most students make. This book will ensure you do just that.

1 | Conceptual Learning and Detail Worrying

There is no point in lying here any longer, you think while staring across the room at the bright numbers of your alarm clock. It's 6:30 a.m., and your alarm isn't set to go off for another fifteen minutes. But you can't fall back to sleep. You're too excited. Today is your first day of medical school class! Coursing energy propels you through your morning routine. You triple-check your backpack before you leave home. "Can't ever have too many highlighters, right?" you mutter to yourself as you head toward the door. You're comforted by the thought that you might reach school early.

Then you're there.

You knew you would get to class early, but this early? It's 7:00 a.m., and class doesn't begin for another hour. Of course, being early is better than being late, but what are you going to do with all this downtime? *Well, at least I'll get a good seat*, you think. As you enter the lecture hall, you see half your fellow classmates are already seated and chatting. "Why is everyone here so early?" you say under your breath. Your plan to sit in the front row has been dashed as it's filled save for those awkward seats on the end that nobody wants. You nestle into the fifth row, next to someone you met at orientation. The conversation quickly moves to how early each of you got up this morning, how neither of you was able to sleep as much as you wanted to last

1

night. Your excitement and anxiety are almost palpable as the clock ticks toward 8:00. The desk barely has enough room for your laptop, notebook, pencil, pens, and multitude of highlighters. Luckily, no one is sitting on your left, so you claim that seat in the name of your possessions. As the clock hits 7:55, the door opens and everyone falls silent. Your professor strolls into the lecture hall and makes a beeline for the computer console. You all watch him intently. As he begins to load his lecture slides, it dawns on you: this is it. You are moments away from starting medical school. You are ready. You have been waiting for this. You want this.

"Today's lecture is on the anatomy of the back and spine," your professor proudly intones. *This shouldn't be so bad*, you think. *How complicated can it be?* Before delving into the material, your professor offers an introductory speech. What he is saying is thoughtful and nice, but it's the same thing you heard throughout orientation. You grow steadily impatient until at last your professor says, "Okay, that's enough of that. Let's start!"

Finally, here we go.

The first few lecture slides are about the different anatomical planes. You're relieved at the thought that this is not an unfamiliar topic. The words *sagittal* and *coronal* recall memories, and you're easily keeping up with the slides. The focus shifts to the spinal cord. You hang on every word. The pace of the lecture seems to have picked up, and you find yourself saying under your breath, "Hey, I wasn't done with that slide yet!" You calm yourself by remembering that all the lectures are recorded online; you can spend time reviewing the slide in the near future. But now you've missed another one because you were too busy thinking about the first missed slide. Your focus intensifies as your brain is confused by words like *efferent*, *afferent*, and *dorsal root ganglia*. Is this even English? With each passing minute, this anatomy lecture is starting to feel like a foreign language class. Peering at the clock, you realize that only fifteen minutes have passed, and you're already hopelessly lost. You can't believe the professor is talking so fast. *I can't possibly be responsible for all this information*, you think as you glance around and see other confused faces. After forty more minutes of a constant knowledge barrage, the lecture is done. You couldn't wait for it to start, but now you're simply relieved it's over.

Once the professor stops talking, you look at the classmate on your right. When you see her looking overwhelmed, you're glad to know you're not alone. Talking to her makes you feel better, knowing everyone is in the same boat. But suddenly your conversation is interrupted. "Okay, this is your first lecture in embryology—let's get started," your professor casually says. "Wait, wait, no! Another lecture already?" you exclaim, and before you can even look at your neighbor, the next hour is underway. By the end of this hour, anxiety is creeping in. You always knew medical school moved at a fast pace, but you had no idea it would be like this. You feel almost as if you're drowning.

The main difference between medical school and undergraduate course study is the sheer amount of information for which you'll be responsible. It is not uncommon for a student to do well in undergraduate courses by focusing on the central concepts rather than worrying excessively about the details. Unfortunately, medical school requires the student to learn the central concepts and to focus on the details, and the number of those details can be, at first, staggering. A popular analogy likens the medical student's efforts to absorb all the information presented in class to trying to drink from a fire hose. Don't feel alarmed if at first you're overwhelmed. Everyone is.

Some medical students worry that they are at a disadvantage to those students who have already taken medical school–like courses such as biochemistry, genetics, and even anatomy. The truth is that even though some may have had a course on a medical school topic, that course was not likely to have included the same volume of detail as a course in medical school. Also, it's likely, particularly if some time has passed since they took those courses, these students have already forgotten the details they did learn. This is not to say they don't have some advantage—their minds are already primed for learning. But the truth is, these students still have to study hard. Don't be discouraged if you majored in history, English, philosophy, music, dance, or any other nontraditional major. After a few months of medical school you'll find your general medical knowledge base is just as good as that of your fellow student who majored in biology. In other words, in medical school, the playing field quickly becomes leveled, and those with a nontraditional major ultimately will be grateful for the fund of knowledge amassed in other fields, making them well-rounded and occasionally providing them insights someone with a purely medical or biological background doesn't have.

Besides, no matter the undergraduate courses taken or the level of preparation felt before school starts, every medical student feels the strain of information overload. So what to do with the colossal amount of information being forced upon you daily? The smartest thing to do is to develop a learning plan. Luckily, medical school faculties want their students to learn, so they try hard to combine information in a way that makes sense. Lectures aren't designed as random assortments of facts—even if at first they sometimes seem to be.

If lectures were truly random, your professor might sound like this: "So here we can see a good example of mitral stenosis. Notice the fish-mouthed appearance of the valve. The Sylvian fissure separates the frontal and parietal lobes from the temporal lobe. Malate follows fumarate in the citric acid cycle," thus leaping from the heart to the brain to biochemistry. You'll discover that won't happen. Each lecture you'll hear in medical school has an underlying architecture. When faculty create a lecture on mitral stenosis, for example, they combine all the facets of the disease and try as best as possible to teach students in a logical progression, usually resulting in a thorough presentation of the topic, containing a mix of concepts and details.

Conceptual Learning

Conceptual learning is special in the sense that it has predictive power. Once you understand a general concept, you can apply it to any specific situation. In other words, if learning can be likened to building a house, the concepts are the beams that hold it all together.

Consider the following two images: (1) a boat with a hole in it and (2) a submerged underwater research laboratory named Aquarius located in the Florida Keys. It probably seems obvious that if a hole is poked in the bottom of a boat, water will rush in. It likely seems less obvious why Aquarius, an underwater laboratory bolted to the ocean floor, doesn't flood when divers enter the hatch from outside. The divers have to get into the vessel somehow, and if that vessel is underwater and it has a hole in it, why doesn't it flood?

You can answer that riddle once you understand the concept that fluids (liquids or gases) flow from areas of high pressure to areas of low pressure. As it turns out, Aquarius has a special room in which the air pressure inside is equal to the water pressure outside. Since there is no pressure difference there is no flow of fluid, so the divers can enter the hatch without risking gallons of water pouring in and flooding the facility.

Let's put a medical twist on this concept. Picture what would happen if there were a hole between the left and right ventricles of the heart (ventricular septal defect). Since blood pressure is normally greater in the left ventricle than in the right ventricle, blood would flow from the left side of the heart to the right. Now imagine the blood pressure in the right ventricle is greatly increased (due, say, to pulmonary hypertension causing the right ventricle to hypertrophy). Though you cannot predict precisely what will happen, you will understand that if the pressure in the right ventricle is greater than that of the left ventricle, blood will flow from right to left. If the pressure in the right ventricle remains lower than in the left, blood will flow from left to right. If the pressures in both chambers are equal, no blood will flow across the defect. Simply by understanding the concept that fluid flows from areas of high pressure to areas of low pressure, you can answer a thousand questions about fluid flow. If instead of learning concepts you attempt to memorize which way the fluid flows in every imaginable situation, you might still be able to answer a thousand questions, but you'll have had to spend your time memorizing a thousand facts. It is plain to see which route is easier.

To shed more light on the topic of conceptual learning, let's play two games. For the first game, you will set a timer for one minute and look at a group of letters. After the minute is up, you will cover the letters, grab a piece of paper, and write down as many letters as you can in the order in which they were presented. Below are twenty-three letters. Ready? Set your timer and begin.

OTTFFSSENTETTFFSSENTTTT

How many did you get? Ten? Fifteen? All twenty-three? You can approach playing this game in two ways.

The first approach is to look at the letters and try to memorize them as best you can. Perhaps you memorized the letters one at a time. Or maybe you turned the letters into words and memorized the funny sentence you concocted. Trying to memorize all the letters is work intensive. It's also the least efficient way to "win."

If you used memorization and were able to reproduce all twenty-three letters, I must compliment the strength of your memory, but now I'll ask you to try a harder game. Being the competitive, type A person you probably are (a common personality type in medical school), my guess is you want to rise to the challenge. So the same rules apply for this game as the last. Try to memorize all eleven rows in order. This time instead of one minute, give yourself four. Set your timer. Go.

1
11
21
1211
111221

3 1 2 2 1 1
1 3 1 1 2 2 2 1
1 1 1 3 2 1 3 2 1 1
3 1 1 3 1 2 1 1 1 3 1 2 2 1
1 3 2 1 1 3 1 1 1 2 3 1 1 3 1 1 2 2 1 1
1 1 1 3 1 2 2 1 1 3 3 1 1 2 1 3 2 1 1 3 2 1 2 2 2 1

Again, this game has two methods for success, but I doubt you were able to memorize your way to victory this time. Although the first game offered a lot of letters, you could turn these into words. This time I've given you far too many numbers. You might memorize the first four lines as one, eleven, twenty-one, and one thousand two hundred and eleven, but after four lines, memorizing in this way becomes cumbersome. If you had an hour to memorize the above lines, you might be able to reproduce them all, but memorization, while sometimes a decent solution, is most often inefficient and least useful for those trying to succeed in learning.

The second method for playing these games involves barely any memorization. Let's examine the first game again. You may have noticed the following pattern:

One

Two

Three

Four

Five

Six

Seven

Eight

...

Twenty-three

In other words, in this collection of letters, each letter stands for a number, starting at one (O) and moving to twenty-three (T). Once you recognize this pattern, you can predict the thirty thousand eight hundred fifteenth letter without any problem at all. Thus the first game is less a game than a puzzle, and once you have puzzled out the pattern, your success at predicting future letters and reproducing those with little effort is assured. Recognizing the pattern in this game is essentially understanding the concept of the solution. Trying to memorize the letters in order requires the same time, focus, concentration, and effort that trying to memorize a slew of facts requires, but learning the concept involved provides you with the ability to answer specific questions about the topic without straining to memorize each letter (or every detail).

Don't worry if you didn't recognize the pattern in this game. I gave you just one minute to play, and I didn't alert you to the fact that it was a puzzle! The only tip-off was the repetition of letters, but you wouldn't necessarily have known that each letter stood for a number. You might have guessed that something fishy was going on since a truly random collection of letters would be unlikely to contain so many of the same letters grouped beside each other. The whole idea here is to show you that seeking to learn concepts will help you tremendously in all kinds of learning situations.

As you may have surmised, the second game involves a trick as well. It is also a puzzle but a much more difficult one. Again, the repeating numbers may have clued you in to the fact that there is a pattern, which is shown below:

1
11   The line above has one one.
21   The line above has two ones.
1211   The line above has one two, and one one.
111221 The line above has one one, one two, and two ones.

This puzzle is significantly harder than the first. The first time I came across it was during my undergraduate physics research. One of my lab

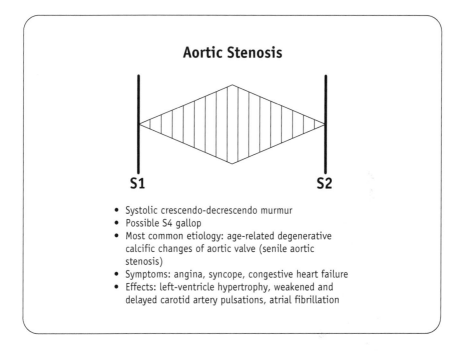

Figure 1.1 Example of a lecture slide on aortic stenosis

mates asked me and the graduate student in charge of the lab to try to solve this puzzle. Needless to say, we got no work done that entire day, so if you solved this puzzle in four minutes, you may just be a genius.

The point of the second game is to demonstrate how difficult it is to succeed through memorization alone. Recognizing the pattern and understanding the concept of how to reconstruct the number strings (the solution to the puzzle) is the only realistic, reasonable, and possible way to reproduce the pattern.

These previous two games show that a concept is much more powerful than the ability to memorize facts. The strength of concepts isn't relegated only to the sphere of puzzles. Rather, it will assure you an easier and more fulfilling way to absorb all the knowledge you will be offered in medical school. So instead of looking at a bunch of numbers and letters, let's now examine the topic of aortic stenosis (fig. 1.1).

Figure 1.1 shows what a medical school slide looks like. Each medical school lecture normally contains thirty or more slides, and you'll usually hear multiple lectures each day. Thus you see the vast amount of information presented in one week. An average test will cover weeks of lectures. I imagine the thought of studying for such a test sounds terrifying, but it's your job as a medical student to understand and remember all the subject material presented to you. You have no choice—you're going to have to retain vast quantities of knowledge in one way or another. And the point of the two games I gave you is to guide you to understanding how to retain the knowledge on aortic stenosis offered on the slide. If you choose memorization as your technique, you'll have to remember that aortic stenosis has a systolic crescendo-decrescendo murmur, with a possible S4 gallop, most commonly caused by age-related degenerative calcific changes, and that it causes left ventricular hypertrophy, as well as weakened and delayed carotid artery pulsations. You'll have to memorize the symptoms, which can include angina, syncope, congestive heart failure, and atrial fibrillation.

You can memorize all this quickly, but remember, you'll be presented with dozens of other slides in this same lecture and have many more lectures to go before test day. You've probably had the experience of going to a party with unfamiliar people and struggling to learn everyone's name at once—one illustration of the fact that our memories aren't perfect.

But just as in the games, there is a way to succeed that's easier than relying on memorization. Take a look at figure 1.1 and see if you can recognize a theme that ties all the information together in a logical way. In other words, is there a guiding principle on that slide that will allow you to predict the presented information about aortic stenosis?

First, think about what aortic stenosis actually is. The aortic valve is the valve that separates the left chamber of the heart from the systemic circulation, meaning that it is the last valve the blood flows through while in the heart. Stenosis is, by definition, the narrowing of a passage. So when a patient is suffering from aortic stenosis, the valve through which the blood leaves the heart is smaller than it should be. If the valve is smaller, more effort will be required to push the blood through it and thus less blood could be supplied to organs that might need it. Therefore, the heart will have to pump harder to push out the blood.

So let's examine the symptoms of aortic stenosis. Angina (heart pain) could result from the combination of the heart pushing extra hard and yet receiving less blood flow. How can the syncope (passing out) be explained? The brain does not do well when it loses blood flow—just a few moments of lost blood flow to the brain can result in syncope, and if the aortic valve is narrowed, the blood has a harder time leaving the heart and moving upward toward the brain via the carotid arteries. Also, this would explain why the carotid pulse is weakened and delayed.

Since the aortic valve is narrowed, the heart must expend more effort to move the blood through it. To understand the effect this might have on the heart, think about what happens to any muscle that works harder day after day. It gets bigger. The only difference between other muscles and the heart is that since the heart is a hollow organ, the extra muscle growth happens on the inside as well as the outside, thus creating less space for holding blood. Since most of the strain will be put on the left ventricle, it will get larger and more muscular, and this explains the left ventricular hypertrophy. When the left ventricle becomes larger and more muscular, it becomes stiffer and is less able to hold a larger volume of blood. An S4 gallop results from a stiff ventricle. The decreased volume of the left ventricle also means that the blood will back up, and where does that backup go? The next place for it is the left atrium. So what happens to the left atrium? With the increased volume of blood it is forced to hold, it will naturally enlarge, and when any chamber of the heart enlarges, there is always the possibility of fibrillation, as the electrical conduction of the heart is a precise matter, and any change in the heart's architecture can throw it out of sync. Since the left atrium is now enlarged from volume overload, atrial fibrillation as a possible symptom of aortic stenosis makes perfect sense.

Thinking about this situation further, you can imagine that the volume overload doesn't simply stop at the left atrium. If left to progress, volume overload will begin to create congestion in the lungs, then the right side of the heart, and then the rest of the body, therefore explaining congestive heart failure.

Can the murmur and age-related degenerative calcific changes also be explained? Since the blood flows through the valve during systole, a systolic murmur makes sense. However, the conceptual learning method isn't perfect; I don't know of a way to logically conclude that the murmur is a crescendo-decrescendo or why the degenerative calcific changes happen, but that leaves just two facts to memorize rather than nine.

Through logical deduction we were able to explain seven of nine facts. While at first, logically explaining the knowledge concerning aortic stenosis may seem more daunting than does memorizing nine details, one of the payoffs of conceptual learning is long-term retention. Seeking to figure out why aortic stenosis causes the problems that it does, and then carefully examining the nature of aortic stenosis and proceeding to logically derive all the conclusions associated with it, enables us to create a true understanding of the condition. This means that just by thinking about it, we have the ability to recall almost all the details, thus removing our knowledge of aortic stenosis from the mercy of our fallible memory.

This process involves understanding the *pathophysiology*, which is just a fancy word for how negative changes to the body take place and the consequences of those changes. If you have ever wondered why your nose runs when you get a cold or why you need to wear glasses, without even realizing it, you have attempted to learn some pathophysiology.

If you are skeptical, you may be saying, "I have a good memory; memorizing nine facts is easy. Why should I waste my time learning the pathophysiology when I can just memorize everything and do just as well on the test as anybody else?" True, memorizing nine facts isn't difficult, but memorizing nine thousand facts is extremely tough. As good as your memory may be, you'll forget things here and there, especially when you're learning new facts every day. In addition, the more facts you try to memorize, the more you wind up forgetting.

The premise of this guide is this: the goal of every medical student should be to understand as much as possible and memorize no more than necessary. For example, let's say you must learn nine thousand facts, and five thousand of these can be predicted by learning the pathophysiology. You'll still have to memorize four thousand facts, but at least five thousand of them won't be subject to the vagaries of your memory.

My example is an arbitrary one, of course. In reality, the proportion of memorized facts to logically recallable facts depends on the subject matter, as evidenced in the two games above. In the first game, if you knew the solution to the puzzle, you could reproduce each letter precisely, with no memorization required. In the second game, if you understood the solution, you'd have only to memorize the fact that the first line was composed of the number one. There is, of course, the possibility of a game at the extreme end of the spectrum—for example, one in which you are asked to memorize pi to sixty decimal places. Since recalling the numbers cannot be done by using reason or logic, you'd obviously have to rely solely on memory.

Let's consider the biochemical subject of human metabolism, specifically the Krebs cycle, glycolysis, the urea cycle, and all that other lovely "garbage." You will have to learn and recall that citrate gets converted into isocitrate, at which point it loses a molecule of carbon dioxide and turns into alpha-ketoglutarate. Also, you'll need to know that NAD+ gains a hydrogen atom and turns into NADH. Every medical student needs to know these facts, and there is no way to reasonably figure out that citrate gets converted into isocitrate (or that succinate gets converted into fumarate). You'll have to memorize those facts, as well as nearly everything else you'll need to learn in biochemistry.

On the other end of the spectrum is cardiology. The human heart is essentially a complicated pump, and the human vasculature can be compared to complicated pipes. If you understand how the heart works (physiology) and what can go wrong with it (pathophysiology), you can logically recall a great deal of information. Being aware of which subjects require memorization and which do not will help you succeed.

Learning the pathophysiology won't just help you recall and remember knowledge. It also will provide insight and predictive power in many different situations because you will be able to connect different areas of knowledge. For instance, if you understand why a certain disease process happens, you may be able to predict the cause of disease in a situation that mimics those conditions. Pure memorization won't enable you to accomplish this kind of thinking.

It is worth asking why we don't use computer programs to diagnose and treat patients. Computers have an advantage over humans in memorization: once a fact is recorded in a computer's memory, it is there until someone decides to erase it (assuming no software or hardware problems interfere). But imagine a group of doctors and programmers developing a computer program designed to fill the shoes of a doctor. First the computer would ask the patient to provide his or her symptoms and medical history. The specific combination of symptoms and details from the history would generate differential diagnoses. Next, the computer would ask appropriate questions to narrow down the list of differential diagnoses. The computer would continue asking questions, attaining the results of a physical exam through robotic methods (use your imagination)—and order any necessary tests, the results of which could be uploaded into its memory. The computer would continue to gather information in this way until only one diagnosis remained. Last, the computer would generate a treatment plan. This seems like it could work.

But what happens if a patient has two unrelated problems? We could run the computer program twice and come up with two different treatment plans. But what if those treatment plans contradicted each other? What if the patient had two related problems that created one unusual complicated problem? Unless the programmers explicitly programmed that specific unusual complicated problem into the system, the computer would come up blank: No solution. And this is because a computer cannot resolve problems outside of whatever it has been programmed to do. Thus our medical computer could not handle novel situations because it hasn't the ability to reason or adapt to new and changing situations.

If you stick to your plan to memorize all the medical facts you can without learning the pathophysiology, you'll wind up no different from our imagined computer. When presented with a new situation, you won't know what to do because you won't have seen this specific situation before. You won't have developed the tools for thinking outside the box, for applying an understanding of concepts to a new presentation. In contrast, if you understand why certain disease processes happen, you'll learn how to make predictions about novel situations. In other words, you'll employ your insight, a gift computers do not have.

Of course, you still must memorize many facts, and to even the most motivated students, the number of facts to memorize may seem daunting at first. Don't be daunted. In chapter 2, "Study Efficiency," you'll learn how to cope with this task.

Detail Worrying

Although conceptual learning is extremely important, some attention needs to be paid to the individual facts that the medical school faculty expect their medical students to know. Nearly every medical school lecture you attend will be riddled with details—all of which the faculty consider fair game for testing. It is, however, a mistake to think that every detail is created equal: some may end up saving a patient's life, while others will almost never be needed. Details can be divided into two categories: useful and useless.

Useful details are those that have at least some clinical importance. Whether that clinical importance is high or low will determine if the detail is of major or minor importance. Useless details are those that have almost no clinical importance, though you may be tested on such useless and superfluous details, which, from this point on, I'll refer to as *microdetails*.

Microdetails have a tendency to occupy a proportionally large percentage of many medical students' study time. They usually show up in one of two ways: contained in a vast chart or list or verbally stated by the professor. During one lecture on cardiac contractility, for example, the professor mentioned that the cardiac myocyte was ideally contracted when its length was two millimeters. Not surprisingly, this fact failed to appear on any lecture slide, class test (although it could have), or board exam I encountered, and it's a fact that is entirely useless to a practicing physician. So why did the professor include this in his lecture? He is a research physician and thought it was worth noting that a cardiac myocyte is ideally contracted to a length of two millimeters. And if you were researching cardiac myocytes, you'd probably want to know the optimum length of contractility. But not one of us listening to that lecture was researching cardiac myocytes at the time, and none of us planned to in the future. The fact was useless to everybody except the professor.

Most medical students react with disdain to being held responsible for knowing extra useless facts, and this one was placed on top of a mountain of medical knowledge under which we were all being buried. But instead of reacting with anger, I imagined this professor working passionately every day, discovering previously unknown facts. I know that when one discovers something new and exciting, that person wants to tell others about it. I'm sure the professor had told his peers about his discovery, but likely few others in his life cared to hear it, and there he was, giving a lecture on his area of expertise and brimming with the excitement of what that knowledge meant to him. Now it's true that some lectures in medical school quickly degenerate into a detailed accounting of the professor's research findings. I know if I'd been doing cardiac research for years on end and someone asked me to present a lecture on the basics of cardiac contractility, I'd have trouble resisting the desire to throw in my own research. You'll want to be aware that these microdetails will, in this way, creep into the lectures you hear. But don't react in anger. Simply understanding their origins will help you avoid that wasted energy.

Microdetails also can arise from a perfectionist professor's desire to cover every aspect of every detail of his or her subject. While some will be useful, microdetails tend to take up residence in long lists, and unfortunately, medical school faculty hold their students responsible for every word on every lecture slide. This means that even the microdetails that show up in long lists are fair game for testing. Worse, faculty might also hold you responsible for the microdetails they mention in class but never include on a lecture slide.

The good news is that microdetails usually compose just 10 to 15 percent of a test, and you can do well without explicitly studying them (see chapter 3, "Diminishing Returns"). You probably wonder how you can tell if a detail is useful or useless. The following list offers you a few ways to recognize microdetails when you come upon them:

- *Microdetails normally do not show up in lecture slides but are verbally stated.* When they are in a slide, they usually are part of a comprehensive chart or list.

- *Professors usually discuss microdetails for a short amount of time.* Since a microdetail is normally a single inconsequential fact, there isn't a whole lot to say about it, so often it's simply mentioned quickly.

- *Microdetails are sometimes off topic.* Such microdetails are normally introduced when a professor has gone off on a tangent talking about his or her research or maybe offering an interesting tidbit of historical information. Regardless, if a detail is off topic, it's probably a microdetail.

- *Microdetails have no clinical consequence.* The human body is a complicated machine with complicated problems, and taking care of a patient is a complicated subject. Clinical care envelops a large body of knowledge that contains many important nuances and details; by definition, microdetails are clinically worthless.

- *Microdetails aren't known with certainty because they concern areas still under active research.* A vast amount of medically related research takes place every day, which means our knowledge of medicine is constantly evolving. The material covered in medical school is always subject to change as a result; in fact, the medicine taught in school is almost always a few years behind the current state of medicine. It takes a while for textbooks, standardized tests, and medical school curricula to incorporate recent discoveries. Sometimes a professor will include the newest medical knowledge in a lecture, but if a professor starts a sentence with "We think that" or "We aren't really sure, but" or ends it with "but no one really knows for sure," you've probably encountered a microdetail.

You need not memorize every microdetail to succeed in medical school, but some students are likely perfectionists and will strive to do so to get the top grade on a test. Since most microdetails are spoken in passing, catching every one can be challenging. Even if you have taken perfect notes and can rewatch each lecture, you may find yourself spending vast amounts of valuable study time on microdetails, and the time spent studying the microdetails can easily eclipse the time spent learning the concepts and important details. Is the extra study time spent learning the answers to 10 to 15 percent of your average medical school test worthwhile? For the perfectionist student, the answer is clearly yes. For most students, however, the answer may not be so straightforward. In chapter 3, "Diminishing Returns," you'll read more about how the nonperfectionist might choose to proceed.

Summary

Learning the concepts and pathophysiology of a topic is extremely important for building a knowledge base that will help you recall information rather than having to memorize it. After learning the concepts and the pathophysiology of a topic, you'll need to memorize any leftover important details. Also, learn to recognize and watch out for the microdetails, the mostly useless details that can, if you're not careful, occupy too large a percentage of your study time.

2 | Study Efficiency

The words in your study guide blur as both eyes decide to stop cooperating with each other. Trying to focus again, you make an earnest effort to understand the sentence you've read over and over for the past five minutes. The word *polyhydramnios* won't sit still under your drowsy vision. One word has turned into two, and they are slowly drifting away from each other. You can't remember the last time you felt this tired.

You gently massage your eyes in hopes that they will wake up again. Alas, it's no use. Their lack of cooperation is a sign that your brain is calling it quits. But the test is tomorrow and you still have lectures to review. *I must keep working, I must focus!* you think. This sentiment used to be a powerful motivating factor, but it is no longer strong enough to overcome the urge to sleep. The sandman beckons—your eyes finally close, having felt as if they were supporting the weight of the world. Your head drops toward the desk. Sleep seems inevitable, but suddenly your legs wake and you stand up. You look like a reanimated corpse, and that's not far from the truth. You feel the rising panic about tomorrow's test, and you know exactly what you need to do. You're lucky you loaded up your wallet with coins and singles this morning as that's the only form of money your drug dealer accepts.

Not surprisingly, the vending machine in the lobby of the medical library has fewer drinks in it than it had at the beginning of the day. You don't really like the taste of energy drinks, but the coffee pot broke a long time ago and no one has since made any effort to replace it. You gulp down the massive drink in just forty-five seconds, and in precisely three minutes you're back in the study room, staring at lecture slides. "All right, let's do this," you mutter as you plug back into your work station. The clock reads 2:17 a.m., and at the sight of it, your stomach wrenches as if you were just punched. The test is in just five hours and forty-three minutes, and the caffeine you just imbibed is barely working.

You struggle through those last few lectures, knowing you won't absorb all the detail you would like to. Of course, looking at the lectures even once is better than not looking at them at all. You hope the test won't have any questions from those lectures, but your inner pessimist raises an anxiety-producing question, "What if there are lots of questions on the test from those lectures?" The last hour of studying is best described as brief moments of anxiety layered upon a background of somnolence.

At 3:26 a.m. you decide the time to sleep has finally come. You've pushed and pushed and you can't possibly push anymore. The last few days of near-constant studying have been brutal on your sleep cycle and general state of well-being. Your brain is like a fully soaked sponge; it has absorbed as much knowledge as it can, and adding more will simply cause other knowledge to leak out. You rise from your desk amid the graveyard of empty coffee cups, energy drinks, and lecture printouts, and like a zombie, you make your way out of the building, muttering something about brains—not because you want to eat them but because yours hurts. You shouldn't drive—you're probably as dangerous as a drunk. But your stubborn nature easily overrides your moral compass as you get behind the wheel. Again, your eyes struggle to stay open as the view of the outside world begins to fade away. Not wanting to die, you panic, and your body offers up a quick surge of adrenaline. You make it home in one tired piece, and one minute later you're in bed. As you stretch out, you make the regrettable decision to look at your alarm clock: 3:54 a.m.

The thought that you have to get up in two and a half hours is disturbing, but you're glad to get any sleep at all. Still, your dreams are plagued by thoughts of the test and all the minutiae you've already forgotten.

Bzzzzz. Bzzzzz. Bzzzzz. You wake up disoriented in the dark, and it takes you thirty seconds to understand that your alarm is going off and you have a test to take. You bound out of bed, pound an energy drink, brush your teeth, and hop in the car. When you reach school, you realize you're almost as tired as you were the night before. Any more studying will be impossible, but a final surge of anxiety-generated adrenaline kicks in, and still sitting in your car, you look over a few study-guide pages one final time. When you step into the building, you hear chattering in the distance. As you move closer to your study room, the din grows louder. It's 7:30 a.m. on Tuesday and the study room sounds like a noisy bar with people trying to talk over one another. You hear angry yelling, but instead of being drunk on alcohol, your fellow medical students are delirious with sleep deprivation. You take a deep breath as your hand rests on the doorknob. You know that as soon as the door opens, you will be bombarded with questions about the minutest of minutiae.

In the room, papers lie everywhere, and the garbage cans overflow with coffee cups. A group of medical students sit around a table squawking at each other. "Hey, do you know why hyperkalemia causes metabolic acidosis?" one of your peers asks you, without so much as a hello or a how are you doing. On test day, medical students have no time for such trivialities. You reach into the depths of your recently learned renal physiology knowledge and your answer makes logical sense. Your sense of self-worth blossoms. Maybe you do know your stuff. Maybe the test won't be that bad. But another peer interrupts and says, "Yeah, that's what I thought, too, but I asked the professor and he said something else, and the book says something different. I e-mailed the professor at 10:00 p.m., but he still hasn't gotten back to me!" You wonder why this student offered up such a baited question. Maybe there is no known answer, and if there isn't, there's a low probability this question will be on the test. Your head feels as if it will explode, so you grab your laptop and leave the study room, heading toward the exam room.

Sitting in your assigned space, you realize that the moment is almost here. You desperately want this test to be over. At 7:50 a.m. the study room group makes their loud entrance. You're sitting beside a good friend, and you focus your conversation on posttest party plans.

Nine minutes pass, and the proctor says, "The test will begin in one minute." The room becomes eerily silent. The anxiety is palpable. A quick check of your carotid pulse causes you to become aware of your accelerated heartbeat. You wonder if it's due to anxiety, excessive caffeine intake, or both. Your stream of thoughts is interrupted as the proctor says, "You may begin your test now. You have two hours."

Okay, this is what I've been preparing for; I am ready for this, you think. You notice the first vignette is lengthy. "A 65-year-old man presents to the emergency department with dyspnea on exertion and complains of..." Oh, and there are so many lab values. Maybe you'll return to this question later. But the next question proves to be just as lengthy, as does the third question. Skimming, you finally find a two-sentence question, an easy one, and answering it generates some momentum. One hour passes and you are on pace to finish with only twenty-three lengthy questions left. You lean back in your chair, take a deep breath, and stretch out your arms. This causes you to become lightheaded, but you hold it together and refocus on the computer screen. Next question.

"A 45-year-old female presents with diffuse muscle pains and complains that...A 45-year-old female presents with diffuse muscle pains...A 45-year-old female...muscle pains." As hard as you try, you can't read that first sentence. You stare harder at the words, but they blur, and you realize it's been a long time since your last caffeine fix. Your eyes start to close and your head begins to droop toward your computer. You can't tell if you're awake or dreaming. The next thing you know, fifteen minutes have somehow disappeared, and you have only forty-five minutes left to answer twenty-three questions. This thought and the catnap you just took create a jolt of energy that powers you through the remaining questions.

Finally it's over. Walking out of the exam room, you let out a sigh of relief. As you make your way toward the study room, the chatter becomes audible, even louder than it was before. As you step into the room, you enter a sea of commotion and questions, with one immediately directed toward you: "What did you get for the question with the woman who had the muscle pains?" Before you try to answer, three people give their answers, each one different. A commotion ensues—arguments, despair, more questions. You want to go home and sleep for three days straight. Lamentably, this afternoon's school activities are mandatory.

You slog from one activity to the next, looking and feeling like a zombie. By some miracle, you make it through the rest of the school day without falling asleep, though the afternoon lectures are a blur, the memory of each immediately erased the moment you leave the lecture hall. Luckily, all lectures are recorded, and you take solace in the fact that you will eventually watch them. Finally, the day is done and you can go home and sleep guilt free. You drink one last cup of coffee for safety's sake and hop in the driver's seat. You've been waiting for this moment for so long, you're ecstatic. Five peaceful hours later, you are staring squinty eyed at the ceiling, somewhat refreshed. Outside it's dark. *How long did I sleep?* Desperately, you shoot a glance at the clock, hoping you can return to a seminormal sleep schedule. When you notice it's only 9:30 p.m., you're relieved. You have just enough time to eat dinner, relax for a couple of hours, and head back to bed.

At 11:00 p.m. you're slumped on the couch, contentedly catching up on all the TV you've missed. You love watching TV without the constantly interfering *I should be studying!* thought. At 11:45 p.m. the grip of sleep begins to take hold, and you decide to finish out the night by fooling around on the computer. You need to check tomorrow's schedule to see how early you need to wake up. You grunt. Class at 8:00 a.m. Looking closer, you see that tomorrow's lectures include multiple hours of relatively complicated topics, but you're almost too tired to care.

At 6:50 a.m. the wretched alarm wakes you. Despite all of yesterday's sleep, you're still in sleep debt, and you'd love to lie in bed a little longer. Somehow you convince yourself that more sleep isn't an option. You head to school, and all day, hour after hour, you're bombarded with medical knowledge. As the day wears on, you realize you're already behind, so later, driving home, you toy with the idea of studying the new material. But once you're home, the motivation isn't there. You want sleep. You get no studying done the rest of the week either. You'd like to study, but you're still drained from Tuesday's test.

Finally, the weekend arrives, and you are excited about taking part in fun activities to make up for the previous miserable all-study weekend. You tell yourself you'll study this weekend, if only for a few hours, but Saturday and Sunday pass and you get no studying done. You tell yourself it's fine. You're only a few days behind and this week you'll make up for that, and with every passing day you repeat the mantra, "I will study."

But studying for the last test took its toll, and even though the somnolence has worn off, the motivation to study isn't there. Three weeks after the test, you can count on one hand the number of hours you've studied. What's worse is that the next test is less than a week away. You begin to panic. You know you have to study and that many sleepless nights and energy drinks are in your near future. The cycle of cramming begins anew. It's as if you are sitting in the middle of a lake in a rowboat with a small hole in the bottom. And as the water flows in, you do nothing but watch it pool beneath you. At first it only coats the bottom of the boat. *Nothing to worry about*, you think. But as more water flows in and reaches your ankles, you think, *I'll take care of this later*. When the water is halfway up your calf and the boat is starting to sink, you yell, "I have to save my boat from sinking!" In a panic you start to bail as fast as you can, and after hurling the last bucket of water out of the boat, you collapse in exhaustion. The problem is, there's still a hole in the bottom of the boat and water is still flowing in. Exhausted, you remain content to watch it rise until once again the boat is sinking.

Most medical students recognize this cycle. Oftentimes they don't study until the last minute, at which point they begin to study excessively. Such students are affectionately known as crammers, and to understand them, let's examine their history.

Why Do Students Cram?

Although students face some tests in elementary school they seldom need to study for them. The first time they take a test that requires some studying is during middle school, and this is also the first time that smarter kids are placed in classes with other smart kids—the first time tests begin to be competitive. Although most of the emphasis in middle school is placed on homework and assignments, tests still count for something. However, most students can easily prepare by studying for an hour or two the night before a test. As a result, in middle school just about everyone is a crammer.

But an interesting change takes place in high school where tests begin to take on much more weight. In some classes, getting decent grades on tests and excellent grades on projects and homework will ensure a good grade in the class, but just as tests rise in importance, so do grades. All high school students know that if they want to go to a good college, they have to get good grades, and in many cases that means doing well on tests. And doing well on tests means being prepared to take those tests. But how much studying does the average student need to do? The answer depends on the student, but two basic patterns of successful students exist: the bright student who tends to cram and the hardworking student.

Once students reach college, the days of waking up early to sit in class for seven hours straight are gone, and even attendance isn't mandatory. Still, college-level courses normally progress at two times the speed of an average high school course. As far as grades are concerned, some consist entirely of test scores, which means if students do well on the tests, they'll do well in the class. College classes also usually have only two or three tests a semester or quarter rather than the multitude of tests given in high school, and fewer tests means that each one covers a wider range of knowledge and therefore requires more preparation. In other words, students must study more than they did in high school to do well on the average college test.

In addition, the level of competition among students in college rises significantly compared to high school. As you well know, acceptance into medical school requires immense effort, particularly since many more premedical students graduate each year than the number of available medical school spots. A premedical student is not only competing with all the other premeds around the country but also with the nontraditional applicants who decide to change careers and have résumés bursting at the seams with fascinating experiences. As a result, premedical students need to consistently do well on hard tests and to take grades seriously. This normally equates to placing utmost importance on studying.

So for the purposes of understanding what leads to cramming, let's look at the two types of students.

The first is the bright student, the student who just "gets it." Bright students usually can get by on their intelligence alone and normally dislike homework and projects since these require "extra work." If it were up to them, their grades would be based entirely on tests, and they usually don't need to work as hard as their peers, which often creates a tendency toward laziness. Through a combination of laziness and decreased study need, bright students usually cram for a few hours the night before the test.

The second type is the hardworking student. Hardworking students may not be as smart as the bright students, but what they lack in intelligence they make up for in hard work. They tend to like projects and homework, where they can spend as much time as they need to obtain superior results. Although they may not "get the material" right away, they will work tirelessly until they do. Usually, hardworking students do just as well as their brighter counterparts, but since they need to work harder to achieve the same results, they learn the value of hard work and have less of a tendency to cram. It's important to note that if you're a smart student, you're not necessarily lazy, and if you're hardworking, you're not necessarily less bright than your peers. Most students fall somewhere between these two extremes on a spectrum. And there are pros and cons to being each type. But the apt question to ask as far as medical school goes is this: Is it better to be smart and lazy or hardworking and less intelligent?

How do our two different types handle the increased pressure to succeed? Bright students are much more at home in the college atmosphere, knowing they can perform above average on any given test. And since most college courses place so much emphasis on tests, bright students have an immediate advantage. They love studying on their own, skipping classes, acing tests, and getting As. On the other hand, since college tests are generally much harder than tests in high school, even bright students have to buckle down and study at some point. This may be the first time in their entire lives that they actually have to study for any significant period of time. A semblance of study habits will begin to develop. Bright students may decide to spread their studying out over time, thus converting from crammers into noncrammers. But some bright students may wait to study until a few days before a test.

In college, hardworking students end up working even harder than they did in high school, making the library a second home. They often talk about how much studying they have to do and how little time there is to do it. The increased pace of class and difficulty of college tests are a strain on hardworking students, and to succeed, they must pour countless hours into studying.

Which type of student makes it into medical school? Acceptance is by no means a linear process, but since competition is fierce, no medical school accepts students who don't have a record of good grades, a good MCAT score, and plenty of extracurricular activities. Thus, premedical students must not only ace every class but also do well on the MCAT and find enough time to participate in other activities.

Doing well in premed classes and on the MCAT generally requires a high level of intelligence, but intelligence alone rarely ensures success—with the exception of the geniuses among us, to succeed in these endeavors, we have to do the hard work. The fact that the premedical student also has to find time to partake in extracurricular activities creates even greater strain, and thus the student who gets into medical school is usually both bright and hardworking.

Figure 2.1 depicts a randomized, even distribution of premedical students with varying levels of intelligence and work ethic. Smarter students are on the right, while those with less intelligence are on the left. Hardworking students are represented at the top of the graph, while lazier students are near the bottom. A smart, hardworking student will end up in the upper right corner, and a smart lazy student in the lower right.

Figure 2.2 illustrates the types of students who normally get accepted into medical school.

As the two figures make vividly clear, far fewer students are accepted into medical school than apply. Usually, only the most competitive make it in. Let's examine the upper right-hand quadrant of figure 2.2. These students have the brain power to give them an advantage on tests and the work ethic to make sure that they are maximally prepared. They always manage to earn As and engage in many extracurricular activities. Note that a large chunk of dots is missing from this quadrant; the missing dots represent students who were smarter and harder working than the average

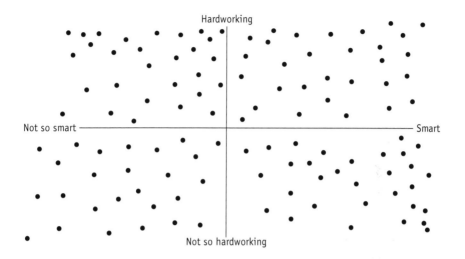

Figure 2.1 Premedical students applying to medical school

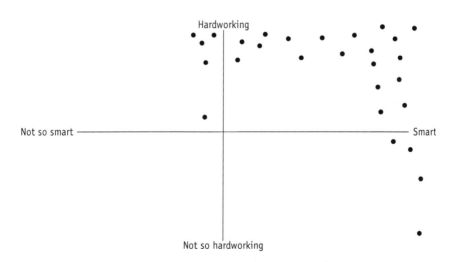

Figure 2.2 Premedical students accepted into medical school

student yet didn't make the cut. They managed to do fairly well in their premed courses, got decent MCAT scores, engaged in extracurricular activities, and probably received a few interviews. Some of these students probably were on a few waitlists. The students in the upper right-hand quadrant who made the cut were either very hardworking, extremely intelligent, or both. The intelligent could get away with working a little less hard than those with less intelligence, but on average, these students were both intelligent and hardworking.

Let's look at the lower right-hand quadrant of figure 2.2. Here many fewer students made the cut. These are the students who many consider bright but who are also lazy. The students from this quadrant who didn't make the cut had the intelligence to do well in class but didn't have the motivation to study hard enough. They typically say things like, "I could have gotten an A in that course if I just studied and handed in all the assignments on time." These students also probably relied on their high SAT scores to mask the multitude of blemishes that marked their high school transcripts. Not surprisingly, they most likely thought a good MCAT score would mask the blemishes of a spotty college transcript. Unfortunately, a stellar MCAT performance does not outweigh poor grades (unless they're in the 99.9th percentile). Students in this quadrant who made the cut were those in the 99.9th percentile on MCAT scores. Considered geniuses by their peers, they also probably get high grades despite minimal studying.

The upper left-hand quadrant of figure 2.2 represents those students who may not be the most intelligent but do work harder than the average student. They usually get decent grades but have a hard time beating the average on any given test and tend to have difficulty with trick questions or problems they've never seen before. Their MCAT scores tend to be average. But these students make up for substellar grades with a multitude of extra-curricular activities, and like their intelligent and lazy counterparts, they face the obstacle that medical schools do not need to accept anyone who isn't strong in all three areas. Realistically speaking, a lot of these students have a difficult time making it into medical school. Those who are accepted are extremely hard workers and lie on the smarter side of the quadrant, the sort of students who are propelled by a fine work ethic and who excessively study for tests. Note the one lone dot near the origin. How did this student, who isn't particularly smart or hardworking, end up getting a coveted medical school spot? The fact is, the admissions process is by no means a linear one; this person is one of the lucky ones. With no outstanding qualities, this student somehow managed to land an interview and ultimately an acceptance. How, you may ask. Your guess is as good as mine.

In the lower left-hand quadrant are the students who are not known for their intelligence or their work ethic. As figure 2.2 shows, not a single student from this quadrant made the cut. Unless one of their parents is the dean of a medical school, the students in this quadrant don't stand a chance. They are not equipped to handle the heavy workload and competition premedical courses demand, and many of them actually drop out of the premedical program.

Now let's get back to the question of why crammers cram. They do so because they have been cramming throughout their lives. Cramming is a habit. Each time they entered a new phase of school (middle school, high school, college) and faced more work, rather than shy away from the challenge, they met it head on, but the habit of leaving all the work until the last minute remained. The only factor that changed was that each stage required more hard work and therefore more time cramming.

So is cramming better than not cramming for medical students? You might answer that the best method of studying is the one that produces the best grades. It may be that two different study methods can produce the same grade, but what about long-term gains? For reasons that will be discussed later, the main long-term gain of medical school studying is long-term retention. When deciding which method of studying is better, consider the following three factors:

- The ability of the study method to produce good test grades
- The ability of the study method to create good long-term retention
- The efficiency of the study method

Grades

Test grades concern most medical students, so does cramming or not cramming produce superior test results? Every medical school test has a finite body of information students are responsible for knowing, and thus your job as a medical student is to be sure you review and learn all the material before test day. Generally speaking, the more you prepare for a test, the better you will perform. (Caution: this association is not linear—see chapter 3, "Diminishing Returns.") The number of hours you choose to study is entirely up to you, but if you wish to obtain a score in the high 90s, you'll have to study a lot more than a student who is content with a score in the low 80s.

Since the ability to obtain a high grade on a test is a question of the number of hours spent studying, whether or not you cram won't matter. If you decide to cram but end up spending four times as many hours studying as a noncrammer, you'll likely obtain a superior test score. In other words, crammers are just as capable of getting high grades as are noncrammers. A test is a measure of one's knowledge of a given material on a specific day, and how you arrived there matters little. No one cares what you knew the week before the test or how much you'll retain a week after. Crammers are experts at making sure they know what they need to on test day since they've been doing this their whole lives.

Long-Term Retention

All medical students wish to become doctors. Some have had that desire for their entire lives. For most medical students, the decision to become a doctor was likely based on two factors: the rewarding nature of the medical field and the respect and compensation doctors receive. Doctors have many responsibilities, but primarily they must provide the best health care they can to patients in need. The human body entails level upon level of complexity and multiple systems influencing each other at the same time. It is probably the most complicated machine we know of, and doctors are presented with the monumental task of understanding the human body well enough to treat all of its potential problems. Obviously, the more doctors understand about the human body, the better they will be able to fix it. Knowledge is what separates doctors of today from healers of centuries ago, who bled people out to get rid of their "bad blood." And where do doctors acquire the knowledge they need? Much of it is acquired during medical school and residency, but to keep up with current treatment modalities and stay on the frontier of medicine, doctors must pursue lifelong learning. In effect, medical training has three periods or stages of learning: medical school itself, residency, and postresidency.

The knowledge learned during these three stages is interconnected. That is, the knowledge you acquire after your residency is built upon what you learn in residency, and the knowledge you learn in residency is built upon what you learn in medical school. Thus, if you forget what you learn in medical school, you've lost your base of knowledge, and grasping, for instance, current treatment modalities for kidney disease will be far more difficult if you can't remember how chronic kidney disease arises in the first place.

Obviously, the human brain is not a computer. Since so much information is being continuously poured into medical students' brains, it is only natural to forget some of it. As hard as you try, you won't remember every detail about every subject, but you need to remember as much as possible of this knowledge base. How can you maximize your long-term retention of knowledge? Two main factors play a role: repetition and caring about long-term retention.

At first, the notion of caring may sound silly. *Surely*, you might think, *every medical student is desperately trying to hold on to everything because that knowledge and understanding are necessary to becoming a good physician*. Sadly, this is not necessarily true. Before medical school, students must take chemistry, biology, organic chemistry, physics, some math, and a little English, but how much of that material must doctors know to do their jobs? Not much, as it happens. Doctors don't have to remember many details of college chemistry; they needn't remember the details of organic chemistry and physics. And guess how much calculus doctors need to know. If you guessed none, you're correct! Much biology needs to be retained, but generally you can forget most of the knowledge you obtain in college with few negative consequences. Once you pass your courses and take the MCAT, there's little reason to retain that knowledge, and most students forget much of what they learned in premedical courses. Obviously, some students remember more than others due to a combination of memory and intellectual curiosity, and it is the latter over which we have some control.

Intellectual curiosity means having questions about the way the world works and wanting to know the answers. Having intellectual curiosity about a subject results in a greater probability of remembering details related to it because genuine interest sparks the mind to retain those details. Imagine that two students who have the same ability to memorize are taking an astronomy course. Student A finds astronomy fascinating, while Student B is taking the class for credit and finds it boring. Student A is more likely to think about astronomy in his free time, and since he spends more time thinking about it, he has a greater probability of remembering the details long term.

Although forgetting premedical subject details has no dire consequences for medical students, simply forgetting everything will prove problematic in that forgetting knowledge can become a habit. This often occurs for those who take every class as a means to obtain a degree rather than for the pursuit of knowledge, and a habit created in undergraduate study will bleed into medical school. Unlike the knowledge learned in premedical classes, forgetting medical knowledge does have serious consequences.

Remembering what you learn in medical school is no easy task, but the first step is to care about the subject matter. The more you care about a subject, the better your chance of remembering it; however we've all had the experience of forgetting something we care about, something that is important to us. Another factor in enhancing memory is exposure. The more exposure you have to a piece of information or knowledge, the greater are your chances of remembering it. In other words, retention comes down to repetition. Just about everyone in this country knows the alphabet, but at some point in your early life, you didn't know it.

Remembering twenty-six new items in order is not easy for any child, but the alphabet song, sung over and over again, helps us. Once we know the alphabet, we use it almost every day, repeating it countless times throughout our lives, thus etching it into the deepest reaches of our memories. Compare this to your memory of an alphabet in a foreign language you once learned. Chances are that you can't remember it unless you speak that language or use that alphabet every day.

Repetition is just as relevant for learning and retaining medical school knowledge as it is for learning and retaining the alphabet. It would be nice if there were a song to aid in remembering the vast amount of medical knowledge—unfortunately, no such song exists—and it is difficult to match the level of repetition most of us experienced with the alphabet. Still, you'll remember and retain material longer the more you repeat it. The literal definition of *cramming* is to force or squeeze an object into an insufficient space; applied to studying, cramming is trying to force or squeeze a certain amount of studying into an insufficient period of time. Thus by definition, cramming assumes a paucity of time, and because medical school lectures contain a great deal of information to learn, going over the material multiple times becomes difficult. Crammers barely have enough time to study everything once, and this means that on average, crammers use little repetition. Little repetition translates to less long-term comprehension, which means crammers will retain far less information than will noncrammers.

One caveat: some people are able to read or hear a piece of information once and remember it forever. This ability is rare, but within the average population is a spectrum of memory abilities, and those with good memories require less repetition to retain knowledge than does someone with a less strong memory. However, in comparing study methods for the purposes of drawing figure 2.3, I assumed the memory abilities of the crammer and noncrammer are otherwise equal.

Indeed, I made three assumptions in creating the figure. The first is that neither student had previous knowledge of the subject matter. The second assumption is that a linear relationship exists between repetition

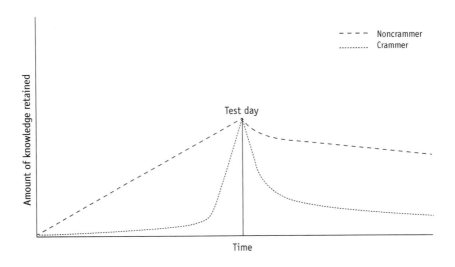

Figure 2.3 Long-term retention: crammer versus noncrammer

and long-term retention of knowledge. (While in truth this relationship is probably logarithmic, with a relative plateau of retention abilities after a certain number of repetitions, for this graph I am assuming that the number of times a medical student reviews the subject material is well below the threshold for the plateau phase and can thus be approximated linearly.) And the third assumption is that the crammer and noncrammer have equal memorization abilities.

You can see that the noncrammer and crammer start on equal ground. As time progresses, the noncrammer studies at a constant rate, while the crammer studies very little. The noncrammer may study a few hours each day, while the crammer attends the lecture but does no other studying. At this point, the noncrammer is gaining knowledge retention through constant studying and repetition, while the crammer is idling. As test day approaches, the crammer begins to study, proceeding from zero to possible all-night study sessions. This progression is visible in the slope of the crammer's line—it is much steeper than that of the noncrammer. As test day arrives, the crammer and noncrammer have reached the same level of retention. This will last just long enough for them to take the test. Following the test, no matter the study method, it is natural for them to lose some knowledge as they quickly forget many of the small details they struggled to remember in the first place. These are the pieces of information that require more repetitions to retain than does the average slice of information. Afterward, we're usually left with a base of knowledge that slowly deteriorates if we do not continue to have repeated exposure to it. As is evident in studying the two lines, the crammer's knowledge after the test drops much more quickly as a result of having done fewer repetitions. Clearly, as time passes, the long-term retention of the material is much greater in the noncrammer.

Thus far, we have determined that cramming and not cramming are equal as far as the ability to produce test grades is concerned, but when it comes to long-term retention, not cramming is a superior study method.

Efficiency

We must ask what makes one study method more efficient than another. The goal of studying is to learn and retain knowledge, and as in all subject areas, the topics in medical school are composed of concepts and varying levels of details. An efficient study method would allow any student to learn the details in less time and would create a better understanding of the subject's concepts than would a less efficient study method.

Let's compare the abilities of not cramming and cramming in helping understand concepts. Every subject is composed of a certain proportion of concepts and details we must learn to master the material. Learning concepts is vital to understanding a subject because those concepts provide the framework that supports most of the details (see chapter 1, "Conceptual Learning and Detail Worrying"). Gaining a conceptual understanding is much tougher than is learning details because it requires us to understand multistep processes as opposed to memorize straight-forward facts. This means we must spend more time learning a concept than learning a detail. Some concepts make intuitive sense and aren't complicated so they're easy to learn, but some concepts are complicated and may take a long time and much studying for us to understand.

A good example of a complicated concept is Einstein's special relativity. A central concept of special relativity is that time is not constant but is based on relative velocity. Suffice it to say that many strange results arise from this concept. One is that the faster one moves, the more time slows from an outside observer's point of view. In other words, if a traveler is moving close to the speed of light while holding a large clock, a stationary observer will see the second hand on the traveler's clock moving much slower (velocity dependent) than the second hand of his or her own wristwatch. However, the traveler will notice no difference in the movement of the clock.

I don't expect a one-paragraph explanation of special relativity to be sufficient for anyone who isn't already familiar with it to understand the concept. Special relativity is complicated, and to truly grasp it you need to spend a lot of time trying to understand it. The point is this: if you were going to be tested on special relativity and decided to cram the night before the test, you would likely fail.

Difficult and complex concepts take time to learn because they need time to settle in the brain. While no concept in medical school is nearly as complicated as is special relativity, many concepts take time to truly understand. A good example is renal physiology. The nephron is a kidney structure with electrolytes that move in and out at different places, hormones that change the balance between absorption and secretion, and many other complicated facets. Because noncrammers spread their studying out over longer periods of time, they would have more time than would crammers to try to learn renal physiology. If the noncrammers didn't understand it one day, they would likely look at it the next day, and if they still didn't understand it, they would study again the day after that. Crammers have only a limited amount of time to study and learn everything, so they do not have the luxury of revisiting the topic. If renal physiology turns out to be hard for them to understand, the crammers—with no time to learn, understand, and review the complexities—would likely not understand the concept and as a result might well fail the test.

A concept can be likened to a plant seed, the soil being your brain. If you want to see a seed become a flower, you need to plant it in fertile soil, water it, and give it time to grow. You can water the seed as much as you like, but without time, the seed will not grow and flower. The same applies for some concepts. You might review renal physiology countless times and still be confused, but one day, for some reason, it will suddenly make sense. The seed was growing, and that day it flowered after having had time to absorb the nutrients you've poured into the soil—time, attention, focus, repetition. But crammers don't have that kind of time. Thus, in regard to the efficiency of learning concepts, not cramming has an advantage over cramming.

Although conceptual learning is important for all medical students, you will not succeed in medical school without learning a multitude of details. Unlike concepts, details—simple facts—can be learned rather easily. The hard part is trying to remember all of them. As discussed earlier, long-term retention of facts is related to repetition, and the greater the number of learning repetitions you do, the better able you will be to retain the details.

I have not yet mentioned the quality of learning repetitions. Not every learning repetition is created equal. So what makes one superior to another? Let's use an example.

Suppose you are given a list of fifty names to memorize. You find a quiet room with nothing in it but a desk, a lamp, and a clock. Assume it is 10:00 a.m. and you are completely rested. This learning repetition will be high quality because you are not tired and you face no distractions in the room. Now suppose you try to memorize the same list of names after being awake for thirty hours and you decide to study in a crowded room surrounded by friends and family. This repetition will be low quality. Clearly, being well rested and studying in a quiet room is much more efficient than being tired and studying in a crowded room.

Although the examples above are extreme, the concept remains true. The more focused and rested you are, the higher the quality of the learning repetition. As to which study method is more efficient for learning details, this depends upon which method of studying provides the best environment for learning repetitions. What kind of learning environment creates the best atmosphere for concentration? Few medical students study in a crowded room with their friends and family, so external distractions are seldom a deciding factor. In fact, most medical students find quiet rooms for studying; most know every nook and cranny of the library and can often be found in some of the most remote and desirable locations. Some people obviously are more capable of focusing than are others, but let's assume that two people have the same level of baseline concentration. What factors could cause one to be less focused than the other?

The ability to concentrate and focus on studying depends on two factors:

- Physical state (how physically tired you are)
- Mental state (how mentally tired you are)

It's not hard to figure out that when you are tired, you cannot concentrate well and will have trouble studying and learning. Common sense dictates that being physically tired results from going to bed too late, waking up too early, or both. Since classes during the first two years of medical school start at the same time for everyone, most students wake close to the same time every morning; thus the differences in sleep will usually result from a difference in the time you choose to go to bed. Cramming requires a lot of studying to be fit into a short time frame, which usually means that crammers have to use almost every available hour in the day to study, often causing them to stay up late. Doing this over and over again causes the average crammer to be much more tired than the average noncrammer. Thus the average crammer will have a lower level of concentration, leading to a less-effective study environment.

As far as mental exhaustion is concerned, consider the following example. Suppose someone gave you a five-hundred-page medical book and instructed you to read it continuously from 10:00 a.m. to 5:00 p.m. Unless you went to bed late the night before, you likely would be well rested during these hours—though reading and retaining knowledge over seven straight hours is tough. At some point your brain would reach a saturation point, like a soaked sponge, and any new information that you tried to absorb would run off. Trying to study when the brain isn't capable of taking in new information is inefficient, and the very nature of cramming requires studying for many consecutive hours in a row, often pushing crammers to the point of saturation and beyond. Although cramming is an inefficient way to learn, if it comes down to either learning something when tired or not learning it at all, crammers obviously will choose the former. In comparison, noncrammers, who spread out studying over a longer period of time, do not have to engage in study sessions that last to the point of saturation. If that renal physiology test, for example, requires forty hours of studying, crammers might put in four days of ten-hour sessions, while noncrammers might put in ten days of four-hour sessions. In those four hours, the noncrammers have a much lower probability of becoming mentally exhausted than do the crammers in their ten-hour sessions. Thus the noncrammers' studying is more efficient than is the crammers'.

Some medical students mistakenly assume that their brains are like machines and can work at the same level of efficiency for as long as they desire. In reality, the brain can be more likened to a muscle. If you overexert a specific set of muscles, those muscles will get tired and will possess less strength over time. But if you rest those muscles, their strength will return. The brain can do only so much learning at one time; after a while, it won't be able to take in new information at the same rate. Stop studying and rest and your brain will recover, and the ability to learn new information will return. Noncrammers rest their brains when they become tired, while crammers force their brains to work inefficiently. Some crammers argue that caffeine provides the ability to remain alert, but while caffeine awakens the body, it does not provide mental rest. The only cure for mental exhaustion is rest, and thus it is clear that not

	Cramming	Not cramming
Ability to produce good test grades	Equal	Equal
Long-term retention	Inferior	Superior
Study efficiency	Less efficient in learning both concepts and details	More efficient in learning both concepts and details

Figure 2.4 Cramming versus not cramming

cramming is superior to cramming when it comes to learning details as well as concepts.

So which study method is better overall: cramming or not cramming? I have compared these two methods in three different categories: the ability to produce good test grades, long-term retention, and study efficiency, and figure 2.4 offers a visual display of the results.

Although the ability of the two methods to produce good test grades is equal, not cramming has the advantage when it comes to long-term retention, and as far as study efficiency is concerned, not cramming is more efficient in learning both concepts and details. I hope by this point you are convinced that not cramming is superior to cramming if you wish to see the best results. If so, you'll want to learn how to become a noncrammer.

How to Be a Noncrammer

The first, and possibly hardest, step in becoming a noncrammer is committing to study in advance rather than leaving everything until the last minute. That may sound simple, but for crammers stuck in the cycle of exhaustion, this can be a tough transition. When you are so burnt out from studying for one exam that you are unable to start studying for the next exam until right before test day, you are stuck in the cycle of exhaustion. You know the symptoms: You're pulling all-nighters right before the test and failing to attend the class after the test, which covers material you need to learn for the next test. Up until just before test time, you're studying as little as possible, and after cramming, you're so tired and burnt out, you cannot find the motivation to start studying again until the fear of the next test causes enough anxiety to restart the cycle of cramming.

The cycle of exhaustion is shown in figure 2.5.

Unfortunately, breaking out of the cycle of exhaustion is not easy, but creating a study schedule is a great start (see chapter 4, "Avoiding Study Anxiety"). Some students may have to gradually wean themselves from cramming, while others may be able to quit cold turkey. Whichever way you choose, it will be a test of your will power.

Once you've made the decision to become a noncrammer, what should you do next? I liken learning in medical school to working in a junkyard. Every day new piles of junk get dumped into the yard, and the medical student's job is to sort through and organize the dump. The longer you wait to begin sorting, the bigger the piles of junk become. If you wait too long, the piles will be too high even to know where to begin sorting. However, if

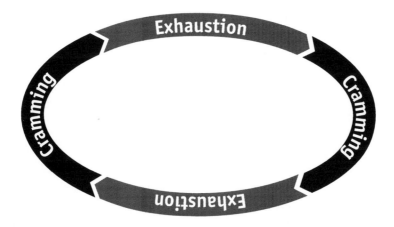

Figure 2.5 The cycle of exhaustion

you sort the piles as they arrive, the job is manageable. In medical school those piles are lecture hours. Learn the information as it is presented, and you won't have to cram later on. For example, if cardiac arrhythmias are taught on Tuesday, before Wednesday you should have a good fundamental understanding of the subject. This doesn't mean your knowledge of cardiac arrhythmias will be perfect; you don't have to memorize most of the details immediately. It does mean that you will understand the major concepts and more important specifics of cardiac arrhythmias. You can memorize smaller details later, when reviewing for the test.

So how do you keep up with the lectures as they are presented? You have two options:

- Learn the material before the lecture.
- Learn the material immediately after the lecture.

If you learn the material before the lecture, you will have a solid understanding of the subject matter once the lecture ends. If you learn the material immediately after the lecture, you will have a solid understanding of the subject matter sometime later that same day. The first method will put you ahead of the game, while the second method will force you to play catch-up. In both methods, you are effectively gaining two learning repetitions.

But is there a difference in quality between these two methods? The subject material in medical school is presented quickly, and absorbing all-new information as it's presented can be difficult. If you're already familiar with the main concepts and details, absorbing the lecture is much easier. If you study the lecture material before the lecture, you'll be able to go at your own pace and spend more time on tricky topics and ideas, thus creating fertile soil upon which the lecture can be planted and will take hold. On the other hand, if you attend the lecture before learning the subject material, you won't have the luxury of being able to spend extra time on those concepts and details you find difficult. You're forced to learn at the pace of the lecture, and if that pace is too fast, or if the lecturer's explanations are confusing, you can do little to remedy the problem.

This effectively creates a lower-quality learning repetition. In learning the material after the lecture, you are effectively getting one low-quality learning repetition and one high-quality learning repetition. In contrast, learning the subject material before the lecture allows you to get two high-quality learning repetitions. So studying before the lecture clearly results in a much higher quality of learning.

Learning before the Lecture

How should you proceed once you've decided to learn the subject matter before the lecture? Should you read the relevant chapter in the textbook? Should you print out the lecture slides and study them? Should you find the lecture from the year before and watch it online? Some people learn better by watching old lectures, while others learn more easily by reading books. The truth is, your method doesn't matter as long as it provides you a good basic level of understanding. You need to know which learning method resonates best with your abilities and stick with that method as much as possible.

Many medical students prefer initially learning from lectures as compared to books because they don't want to get bogged down in the multitude of details presented in books. This is understandable, but a problem arises when a lecture is of low quality. Medical schools employ many lecturers, and while all are knowledgeable, most are researchers or doctors first and teachers second, and the quality of lectures varies greatly. If you decide to study only from lecture slides, learning topics that are taught through a poor lecture will be tough. On the other hand, if you're flexible, you can always substitute a bad lecture with a good book, one that explains the subject matter logically and thoroughly. Reading a book often gives you an opportunity to see the whole picture and to fill in any gaps a faulty lecture might have left behind, but you need not memorize every detail in the book.

Note Taking

Most medical students are predisposed to taking copious notes because they have been doing so their whole lives. Those who neglected to take good notes for a lecture learned they had to rely on their memory or find someone from whom they could borrow notes. These days, most medical schools record their lectures, thus providing perfect notes—an exact replica of the lecture! So does taking notes make sense?

That depends. Oftentimes the physical act of writing something down helps in recalling the information. Still, one mistake some students make is to focus so closely on writing down everything that they don't process what they are listening to. (This type of student carries a dozen highlighters and is more focused on using the right color than in hearing what the lecturer is saying.) Taking notes to augment learning makes sense as long as the note taking doesn't distract you from also paying attention. The point is to make sure that your note taking is actually helping you learn rather than being a compulsive and habitual activity.

Nearly every medical student at some point makes the mistake of studying while tired. Crammers are more predisposed to this problem than are noncrammers, but it can happen to anyone. Since medical school classes start relatively early in the morning and activities often last late into the afternoon, sleepiness is a normal state for medical students. But as I said earlier, studying while sleepy is inefficient—a poor use of your time. The key is to realize you're sleepy and to delay studying until you are mentally awake. Some medical students take naps; some drink caffeine. What you do is a personal decision and one that may require some experimenting. I learned that I never needed more than a half hour of nap time to shake off the mental fatigue enough to study. The desire to sleep longer was always there, and naps can be a pitfall if you're someone who is incapable of taking catnaps. I'm sure you've heard more than one of your peers say at some point, "I just wanted to take a short nap, but I ended up sleeping for five hours." Long naps are inefficient. Most of the time, a long nap will throw off your sleep schedule and create fertile ground for staying up too late, which inevitably leads to future sleep loss. For those incapable of taking short naps, caffeine may be a better option.

By studying day to day to keep up with lecture material as it is presented, you will create a good fundamental understanding of every topic's major concepts and details. Alas, even with consistent studying, you'll want to review many details before a test. The grade you desire will determine how much time you need to spend reviewing those details (see chapter 3, "Diminishing Returns"). Fortunately, the whole process will be much easier once you have learned all the major concepts and details, which will provide a structure upon which the small details will take hold and cling. In other words, you've already done most of the work. Creating a reasonable study schedule will help you efficiently retain the small details without overburdening yourself (see chapter 4, "Avoiding Study Anxiety").

How do you go about studying all those details? Simple. Look at each lecture slide and make sure you have memorized the relevant details. Almost all medical students will concomitantly make a study guide while memorizing those details, and this will help condense the content to an easily reviewable form.

Summary

Not cramming provides greater long-term retention than does cramming and is overall a much more efficient study method. However, becoming a noncrammer is difficult because cramming is a habit that can be hard to break. Choose the study material (book or lecture) from which you learn better. (If you need to practice to discover which is better for you, do so.) Also, learning the subject material before a lecture is more efficient than learning it afterward, and note taking should not get in the way of paying attention and learning. Lastly, avoid studying while sleepy.

Slipping back into your cramming ways, particularly if you have gotten by with this method for years, is easy. You must expend real mental effort to stay on top of the mountain of information continuously presented in medical school. The benefits and efficiency of not cramming are many, but only you can decide what works best for you. Being flexible and knowing when something isn't working and needs to be changed is vital, and it's important to understand that your study method for the first test may be vastly different from your study method for the last test. The key is to continuously evaluate your method of study, see what can be improved, and adjust accordingly.

3 | Diminishing Returns

Those first couple of months were rough. Thankfully, it's getting easier. You are finally getting used to the increased strain of medical school, and by now the shock that you felt while taking your first test has dissipated. You remember staring in awe as some of the minutest of minutiae revealed themselves as test questions. You thought, *How could they possibly ask me that?* Recovering from that experience took some time. Your test score wasn't the lowest in the class, but it could have been higher. The second test was much better since you knew what to expect and changed your study focus accordingly. You started keying in on the smaller details instead of just studying the main concepts and ideas. This new attention to detail caused your study time to nearly double. And even though your second test score was significantly better, it was still a couple of steps below those of a few students who always sit in the front row. *How do they do so well?*

You know you should be concentrating on this Krebs cycle lecture. This might be the third or fourth time you have "learned" about the Krebs cycle, yet it all seems mostly unfamiliar. Remembering the details of the Krebs cycle is almost impossible; you might as well try to memorize the distribution of lines on a bar code. Still, here you are again, only this time the lecture has far more details than it ever had before. You have a test coming up in two weeks on a ridiculous amount of biochemistry, and realizing this causes a knot in your stomach. Forget about going out this weekend. Even if you do somehow manage to free up some time, it's doubtful that anyone else will. Everyone will be studying.

As you begin to focus on the matted red hair of the student in the front row who always manages to get the highest grade, you let out a deep sigh. *How does he do so well?* You begin to wonder if he has some sort of secret study method or if he is getting the tests ahead of time. The intonation change of the professor's voice, along with the pure black lecture slide, signals exactly ten minutes until the next lecture begins. The lecture hall quickly empties—many of your peers drank too much coffee this morning. You decide you need a good stretch and some sunlight, so you step outside into the crisp autumn air. It seems one of your classmates had the same idea. You exchange hellos with squinty eyes. A conversation about medical school quickly develops and, of course, leads to discussion about the upcoming test and how much studying you both have to do. While you both mourn the loss of the upcoming weekend, the student with the matted red hair opens the outside door just long enough to see both of your faces. He says nothing and slips back inside.

"That was weird," you say.

"Yeah, that guy doesn't like spending too much time around others. He's insane."

You can't help yourself: "How does he always do so well on the tests?"

"Oh man, you should see how much he studies."

Your new friend begins to talk about the obsessive nature of the red-haired student's study method. A quick calculation reveals that he studies almost twice as much as you do.

"I can't believe he studies so much!" you gasp.

"Yeah, it's crazy. But he does so well on the tests, I'm thinking of ramping up my studying, doing some of what he does. I just want to do well, you know?"

You stare blankly at your friend, who just admitted he wants to participate in insanity. A quick glance at your watch reveals that the next lecture is going to start any minute. You both walk back inside amid a score of tired faces and groans. As you take your seat, you try clearing your mind to prepare for the next hour of biochemistry. One thought won't let you focus: *Should I be studying more?*

Every medical student knows a significant amount of time will be spent studying and that some weekends will be sacrificed. Most medical students want to do well and are under the impression that to do so, they must spend vast periods of time studying. Most commonly believe that the more they study, the better they will do on a test—the woman who studies for ten hours should do better than the man who studies for five. But will the ten-hour student's score double? If you study for seventy hours for a test, is hour sixty-seven as fruitful as was hour five? Will the material you studied during hour five produce more points on the test than the material you studied during hour sixty-seven? Figure 3.1 illustrates the idea that studying is a linear process.

In figure 3.1, hours spent studying equate to the test score. In this model, the student who desires a perfect score must study for one hundred hours, while the student who wishes only to pass needs to study for just seventy hours because the points earned from studying in hour five equal the points earned from studying in hour sixty-seven—in other words, one hour studied equals one point earned. Hour five raises your score from 4 percent to 5 percent, and hour sixty-seven raises your score from 66 percent to 67 percent. But is this what actually happens?

The problem with the graph in figure 3.1 is that it is based on a few false assumptions. The first is that during each hour of studying, you will come across one point of learning that will produce a single test point. But what if during hour six you learned a central concept that appeared seven times on the test, while the content you learned during hour eighty-five failed

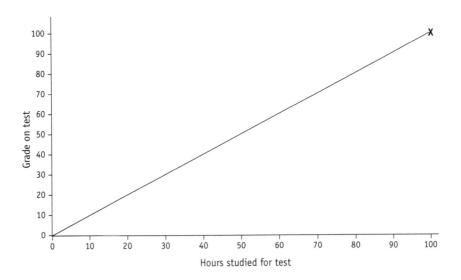

Figure 3.1 Test grade versus study hours—linear relationship

to show up on the test at all? In that case, in terms of the score, hour six would be fruitful, while hour eighty-five would be almost entirely useless.

The fact is, all study hours are not equal, and the relationship between hours studied and test score is not linear. Here's a more realistic example of the relationship between hours studied and score. For simplicity's sake, let's look at a test with only ten questions for which you spent ten hours studying and for which you received a perfect score. If some study hours were more productive than others, the graph would look like figure 3.2.

What is immediately apparent in this graph is that the relationship between hours studied and test grade is stepwise rather than linear. Note that study hour seven (the studying done from 6:01 to 7:00) covered topics that showed up in three test questions, while hours four, six, nine, and ten covered no test question topics. In other words, if somehow you had skipped those four hours of studying, you would have received the same test grade for having studied just six hours as compared to ten.

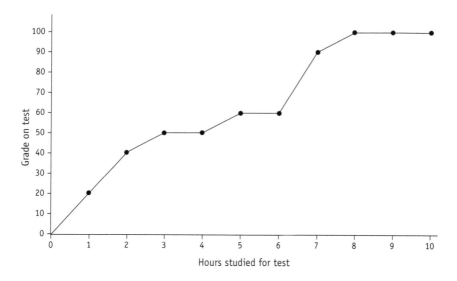

Figure 3.2 Test grade versus study hours—nonlinear relationship

High-Yield Material

The truth is that some material appears in more test questions than other material. A popular medical student term for this heavily tested material is *high-yield material*. The idea behind high-yield material is that the time spent studying it will, on average, yield more points on a test than will the time spent studying non-high-yield material. So how do you determine whether topics of knowledge are high, average, or low yield?

Medical students often are left in the dark as to the precise details that will appear on a test. On occasion, I studied material that I thought I would surely be tested on, only to see no trace of it on the actual test. A few times when I ignored what I thought to be a useless detail, I was distraught to see it involved in multiple test questions. Medical school faculty purposely leave students in the dark because they want them to study *everything*, and as a result, almost every test you take in medical school will contain multiple questions on minute details. Since eventually every medical student comes to understand that every detail covered in

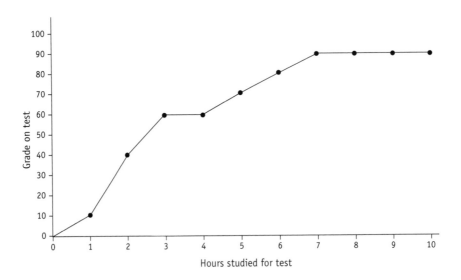

Figure 3.3 Test grade versus study hours—Alice

a lecture could possibly show up on a test, most of them attempt to study everything—no easy task. So what to do?

Let's look at an example of a ten-question test that had nine questions of acceptable difficulty and one question that was almost completely unreasonable because it was based on an obscure microdetail. For this example, we'll look at two students, Alice and Bob. Alice is a smart young woman who leads a balanced life. She wanted to do well on this test but is no perfectionist. She decided she would be content with a grade of 90 to 100 percent. Alice's parents were coming to town that weekend, so she decided she had just ten hours to spend studying. Her "test grade versus study hours" graph looks like figure 3.3.

Alice studied the major concepts and details but ignored most of the microdetails, and she reached her goal (while not getting a perfect score). As figure 3.3 shows, Alice hit a plateau in her study productivity during hours eight to ten. If Alice had known that she would gain no more test points from those later hours of studying, she

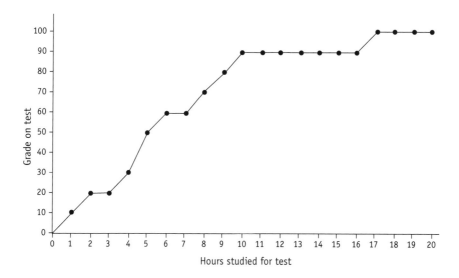

Figure 3.4 Test grade versus study hours—Bob

could have stopped studying as soon as she reached the seven-hour mark and received the same grade. If Alice had done this, she would have had an extra three hours to sleep, do some exercise, and spend with her family.

Now let's take a look at Bob. Bob is also smart, but he unfortunately suffers from perfectionism. Bob can't settle for anything less than 100 percent. He decided that since most people were studying ten hours for this test, he would study twenty. (Does this sound like anyone you know?) Bob's graph of "test grade versus study hours" looks like figure 3.4.

Bob studied all the major concepts, details, and microdetails and succeeded in achieving his goal of 100 percent, but let's examine what he had to do to reach this goal. By the end of the tenth hour, he had the same grade as Alice—90 percent. To elevate his grade from 90 percent to 100 percent, Bob spent seven extra hours studying until he came across the microdetail that appeared on the test. On top of those seven hours, Bob spent another three studying—hours he could have used for more pleasurable activities. Because we have no way of knowing when we'll come across a specific microdetail on a test, the only way to make sure we can answer any question that could possibly be asked is to study every single microdetail ever presented. That is what Bob did. That's why he got 100 percent.

I'm describing the principle of diminishing returns, a principle that holds just as true for medical school tests as it does for anything else. Here's an analogy that may provide perspective. Picture a giant glass jar filled with glitter sitting on a table in a fully carpeted room. Imagine someone walking into the room, picking up the jar, and hurling it to the ground. The glass jar explodes, and a cloud of glitter disseminates around the room, covering the carpet. The mischievous person who broke the jar looks down. The comedian Demetri Martin once quipped, "Glitter is the herpes of craft supplies," and as the hurler looks down, he realizes how true this is and how impossible it will be to clean up the mess. So what to do? Chances are, a fair proportion of the glitter has fallen into large piles, and those might be the first places to tackle. Perhaps some of the piles are big enough to be removed mostly by hand. Next, our mischief-maker might vacuum to remove the smaller piles, but even a thorough vacuuming will leave behind some tenacious specks. Let's say that 5 to 10 percent of the glitter still remains dug into the carpet. To clean up that last percentage, the cleaner would have to move slowly around the room, examine every inch of carpet, and pick up every last speck. This likely would take considerably more time than all the previous steps combined. In effect, most of the time spent cleaning would be utilized in removing the smallest portion of glitter.

Studying for a medical school exam can be like trying to clean up glitter. The big piles of glitter are the central concepts, the smaller piles are the details, and the little stubborn specks left behind after vacuuming are the microdetails. If you're like Bob and you want a score of 100 percent, you'll spend most of your study time finding and memorizing the microdetails. Figure 3.5 shows a pie chart of your study time.

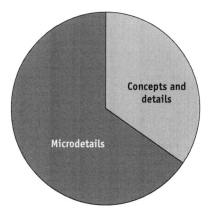

Figure 3.5 Breakdown of study time to attempt a perfect score

But as a rule, microdetails usually compose just 10 to 15 percent of an average medical school test, while concepts, major details, and minor details compose the other 85 to 90 percent. That means that those intent on receiving a perfect score commit most of their study time to the last 10 to 15 percent of possible points. For some, those last points are worth the countless extra hours of studying, while others would prefer spending their time in other ways. The truth is, if you ignore most of the microdetails but master the central concepts and details, you will perform only slightly worse than will a student like Bob.

The principle of diminishing returns means that the closer you come to 100 percent, the harder the points are to gain. Consider the following illustration. Imagine a medical student who decides to take a one-hundred-question test without studying at all (medical school suicide). Almost all medical school tests are multiple choice tests (save for some anatomy tests), with four or five answer choices for each question. Probability alone says that just guessing will yield a score of 20 to 25 percent, thus making those first percentage points free points. The student will likely get them just by showing up for the test and properly filling in the bubbles.

Now suppose our medical student decides to put in minimal effort toward preparing for the test, showing up for every lecture and taking notes but doing nothing beyond that. This time he will probably be able to rule out clearly wrong answers and will likely get a portion of the easy questions correct—let's say 25 percent. Since he is guessing on fewer questions, the number of points from guessing will be 15 to 18.75 percent, and the total score will be 40 to 43.75 percent, as explained below.

Number of questions the student knew the answer to: 25

Questions he guessed on: 75

Probability of getting the guessed questions right:
20 percent to 25 percent

Guessed questions that were right:
[75 x 0.2] (questions with five answer choices) = 15
[75 x 0.25] (questions with four answer choices) = 18.75

Total number of questions correct:
[25 + 15 = 40]   Grade: 40 percent
[25 + 18.75 = 43.75]   Grade: 43.75 percent

This means that just by attending class, our medical student was able to increase his score from 20 to 25 percent to a possible 40 to 44 percent. While he did not study outside of school, he did spend a fair amount of time in classes, so raising his grade to 40 to 44 percent required a substantial investment of time.

Now let's say that our medical student feels motivated enough to attend lectures and to study outside of class. He still lacks the motivation to study everything in depth, and he gives some topics only a cursory glance. Still, he is able to learn the concepts while ignoring some details and all microdetails. Assume his studying is sufficient to enable him to correctly answer 65 percent of the test questions. Now his grade will be 65 percent plus the percentage of correct guesses on the remaining 35 percent of questions as shown below.

65 percent + (35 percent x .2) = 72 percent
65 percent + (35 percent x 0.25) = 73.75 percent

A passing grade! By studying, our medical student was able to increase his test score by around 30 percentage points. Note that the amount of effort put in to achieve this higher grade has also greatly increased. The first 20 to 25 points required no effort, the next 20 points required a significant amount of time spent in class, and the last 30 points required a fair amount of studying time added to this mix.

Let's take this one step further. This time our medical student commits to hitting the books and decides to study the concepts and details three times. He doesn't spend a lot of time learning the microdetails. Through all these efforts, he acquires enough knowledge to answer 87 percent of the questions correctly. Now his test grade is calculated as shown below.

87 percent + (13 percent x 0.2) = 89.6 percent
87 percent + (13 percent x 0.25) = 90.25 percent

Our student has gone from barely passing with a score in the low 70s to earning a respectable grade. Of course, the later points did not come easy. He had to study three times as much to get 90 percent as compared to 70 percent. Again, the first 20 to 25 points were free, the next 20 points required some work, the following 30 points required a considerable amount of work, and the last 20 points required three times the effort and time.

Dare we ask what our student needs to do to earn those final 10 points? At this point he knows all the concepts, details, and minor details well and can probably correctly answer any question related to them. To further increase his score, he'll need to incorporate microdetails into his studying. This means he needs to know every little fact ever mentioned in class even once. In other words, he has to memorize everything! He can forget about a social life, about having a significant other, and about almost any pleasurable activity he might once have enjoyed. It all

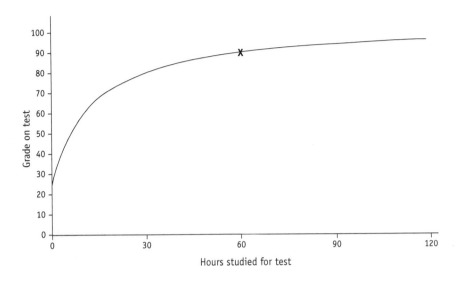

Figure 3.6 Test grade versus study hours—diminishing returns

comes back to the idea of diminishing returns. The points closer to 100 percent are the ones that are harder to gain. Thus, the most realistic representation of the "test grade versus study hours" graph would look like figure 3.6.

Earning the first 25 percentage points as illustrated in figure 3.6 requires 0 hours of studying. After 25 percent, the line rises rapidly as the central concepts and details are learned. Somewhere around hour 20 (an arbitrary choice, although not uncommon), the student reaches 70 percent. Notice that the rate of grade increase becomes smaller and smaller as more hours are spent studying. The most important aspect to notice is how the graph begins to level off once we reach 90 percent and a correlation to 60 hours spent studying. At this point (X), studying is directed toward finding and memorizing the microdetails, and the returns become greatly diminished. Many extra hours of study are required for minimal gain.

In my experience, X is the ideal stopping point. In this example, hours 0 to 60 raise the score from 25 percent to 90 percent, while hours 60 to

120 bring just a 5 percent rise. Study hours from X onward are largely inefficient. Of course, the specific numbers will change depending on the test taker and the difficulty of the test, but the concept of diminishing returns will hold true. One might argue that the person who studied 120 hours will have greater long-term retention than will the person who studied just 60 hours. However, this isn't as cut-and-dry as you might think, and the outcome depends a great deal on the methods of study (see chapter 2, "Study Efficiency"). Suffice it to say for now that there are diminishing returns with both exposure and memory. Studying a topic twice will provide much greater retention than will studying a topic once, and studying a topic three times will provide better retention than studying twice. But will studying a topic five times be much different from studying a topic six times? It's hard to say, but if there is a difference, it will probably be minimal. Each successive study session is less productive than the one before it—another illustration of the principle of diminishing returns.

Summary

The principle of diminishing returns is just as real for medical school tests as it is for anything else. The closer one gets to perfection, the harder it becomes to achieve it. You'll be required to spend more time to earn those last ten points on a test than you'll have spent earning the previous ninety. That is not to say that going after those last ten points isn't worthwhile. Some students believe it is well worth it. You must decide if you wish to achieve perfection, but regardless of whether or not you desire to become the top student in your class, being aware of the principle of diminishing returns will provide you with realistic expectations.

A Quick Note on Anatomy

By far one of the most unique experiences first-year medical students can have is working in the gross anatomy lab. From the potent smell of formaldehyde to the chill of the ventilation, the anatomy lab provides a visceral experience that is hard to forget. The thought that the cadavers on display were once living beings and are now about to be dissected can overwhelm even the most stoic student. Human anatomy is hard enough to learn when displayed neatly in a book, but combining it with a cadaver can unsettle anyone. What's a first-year medical student to do? Should she spend every available minute in the lab? Or should she just learn anatomy from a book and hope everything will look the same on the practical examination?

The best way to learn anatomy is using both methods—dissecting cadavers and studying the book. The least efficient way to do this is to simply show up in the anatomy lab unprepared. To avoid wasting time, you need to enter the anatomy lab with a plan. If you don't know what you're looking for, you can waste countless hours in the lab looking at pictures and hoping you don't cut something vital. If you're already familiar with the anatomy you're trying to learn, both the dissection and identification will proceed more quickly and smoothly. Learning the anatomy from a neatly displayed and labeled anatomy text takes less time initially than does learning on a messy, unlabeled cadaver. Thus, the most efficient way to approach the anatomy lab is to first learn what the anatomy is supposed to look like by studying textbooks or lecture slides. Once you know what things are supposed to look like, you'll have an easier time recognizing those parts in the cadaver.

Most medical students usually ask what kind of time they need to spend in the lab. Some students seem to practically sleep there, while others seldom show up. We've already established that those who have studied and are familiar with what the anatomy is supposed to look like will spend less time in the lab. But suppose you already know the anatomy reasonably well. How much time should you spend with the cadaver, considering that you will be responsible for knowing a long list of items? Some of these are easy to find (large muscle groups), while others are damn near impossible to find (small nerves). Of course, every cadaver is slightly different, so while one muscle may be hard to find in one cadaver, it could be easy to find in another. For this reason, it's wise to make every effort to examine a few cadavers. Know that some items are almost impossible to find no matter which body you choose to examine. Many medical students end up spending large amounts of time looking for almost-impossible-to-find structures such as the thoracic duct. The question becomes whether you should spend extra time trying to identify every single structure.

Not surprisingly, the principle of diminishing returns applies here as well. If you wish to find every item on every list, you'll spend most of your time searching for the harder-to-find items. Think of this as searching for the proverbial needle in a haystack. Suppose you really want to find the *ligamentum teres* and decide that you won't leave the lab until you've found it. You might end up spending a half hour searching multiple bodies before you finally identify this structure. You need to ask yourself if the discovery of the *ligamentum teres* is worth half an hour of your time. For those bent on achieving a perfect score, the answer is yes. For most other medical students, the answer is no. If you know the anatomy well, you can assume that the harder an item is for you to find, the harder it is to find for the faculty as well. This doesn't mean the *ligamentum teres*, for example, won't show up on a practical exam; it just means that it has a lower probability of showing up. In my experience, having studied anatomy thoroughly, when I was unable to find an item on an already-dissected cadaver in under a minute, it seldom showed up on the exam.

4 | Avoiding Study Anxiety

Wednesdays are long days, but thankfully you have just thirty minutes left of class. The clock strikes 4:00 p.m. and you let out a long sigh of relief. At this point the seconds feel more like minutes; it's as if the clock purposely slows down when it knows someone is watching it. Hoping to move time a little faster, you make an earnest effort to pay attention to your professor's lecture, but you've been listening to this type of thing all day, and your eyes and ears no longer want to cooperate. The slightest distraction draws your attention away: *When did Brian get a new phone? Oh yeah, he lost his other phone the other night at the bar. What was that horrible-tasting drink I had there? Maybe—* All of a sudden, the change in the professor's intonation catches your attention: "And that's it for today." Whoa, that last half hour went by a lot faster than you thought it would.

Standing up in a hurry causes you to feel lightheaded. The world around you becomes fuzzy and you're aware of the lack of blood flow to your brain. You grab your things and you lazily make your way out of the building while conversing with those peers who happen to be walking out with you. After tossing your belongings onto the backseat of your car, you collapse into the front seat. Turning the ignition, you discover you are staring into space. It takes a full minute before you are able to snap out of your trance and put the car in reverse. *I must be pretty tired,* you think. *Maybe I'll take a short nap when I get home.*

As you pull into your apartment complex, a quick glance at the car dashboard reveals that it's precisely 5:02 p.m. You figure you have more than enough time to take a short nap before commencing studying.

Strangely and pleasantly, the thirty-five-minute nap you take feels long. As you groggily open your eyes, you lament silently that the sunlight has disappeared. You shoot a glance toward the alarm clock. It reads 7:16, and your jaw drop is almost audible. "Oh man, I can't believe I slept for two hours!" Your stomach begins to wrench as you see that the day is slipping away.

In a combination of frustration and stupor, you make your way to the shower, hoping the water will wash you awake. Thankfully, it does the trick. You feel refreshed and ready for action. Alas, the moment of relief is short-lived as you realize how much studying lies ahead. Again your stomach turns.

You throw on your everyday afternoon pajama attire and plop down in the desk chair. Your desk can best be described as an organized chaos of papers; the untrained eye would see only disarray. But to you, everything is right where it needs to be. Every study material you need is displayed, and there before you is something else: the TV. And the Internet. You knew placing the TV in front of your desk was a bad idea, but it's too late to move it now. The daily battle picks up right where it left off yesterday. Part of you wants to study, but most of you doesn't want to. The thought of watching TV has never been so enticing, but you know once you turn it on, it won't go off easily. The *I need to study* thought seems to be winning over the *I want to watch TV idea* and with great effort you open a book, but you say, "Ugh, I really don't want to read this now." Procrastination gains the upper hand, convincing you that spending a few minutes on the Internet is a good idea. As always, a few minutes turns into ten, which bleeds into thirty.

Shooting another glance at the clock, you notice that it's 8:20 p.m. A moan escapes your lips and the sight of the biochemistry textbook causes physical distress. Your stomach now feels like someone has punched it. "Okay, I'm really going to start studying now." In anger and frustration, you slam your book on the desk and open it to the proper page. With your brain poised for action, your gaze steadily moves across the text. Slowly, the anger and frustration melt away as both the pages and time seem to slip by. And then out of nowhere, your stomach begins to act up again. This time it doesn't feel like someone punched you when you weren't looking. No, it is the unmistakable feeling of hunger. "Okay," you say, "I'll just eat a little something and then get right back to studying." Looking again at the clock, you notice that only fifteen minutes have passed since you started reading. Frantically, you count back through all the pages you have read. "Only three pages!" you yell. "It's been three and a half hours since I came home and I've barely done anything!" Your stomach now feels like a donkey kicked it. That pain, combined with the pangs of hunger, is almost too much to bear.

Eating is now the number one priority. The thought of cooking doesn't even enter your brain. You rummage through your freezer and discover, luckily, you have enough Hot Pockets and frozen pizzas to last for weeks. Part of you knows eating frozen food this often isn't healthy, but your busy schedule leaves little choice. Twenty minutes and two Hot Pockets later, your stomach starts to relax. "Time to get back to the books." As much as you want to start studying, your full stomach won't yet allow it. You convince yourself that some digestion time is necessary. "It's 8:55 now, so I'll just watch ten minutes of TV and then get back to studying." You know that most reality shows are crap, but they are so addicting. Unfortunately, television wasn't meant to be watched for ten minutes at a time, and doing so takes a strong will. Time slips by as you decide to watch the next episode of some marathon. You know that watching this much TV is a bad idea, but generating enough momentum to propel yourself off the couch is impossible. Little by little, that uncomfortable feeling in your stomach starts to become ever more noticeable. It tends to arrive in waves, mostly during commercial breaks, when the thought of all the studying that hasn't been done boils to the surface.

Minute by minute passes as you sit in front of the TV and your anxiety level rises. The sad realization dawns upon you that it is already 11:03 p.m. and you've read just three pages. Now it feels like someone took a sledgehammer to your gut. In desperation, you make a beeline toward your biochemistry book, quickly find where you left off, and start to read again. The television is off, your laptop is closed, and it seems that you will finally be able to get some studying done. Ninety minutes and twenty-three pages later, the study anxiety you were feeling has faded away. Unfortunately, it has been replaced by the *Oh no, I'm not going to get enough sleep because I stayed up too late studying and I'll be exhausted tomorrow* thought. Luckily, there is a simple solution for this type of anxiety. Nestled in bed, physically drained from the day's activities, despite the two-hour nap that you took, you think about tomorrow's jam-packed day. This only raises your anxiety level higher, but now you're almost too tired to worry. Happy to be in bed, you barely care what time it is. Until morning, you are free from responsibilities.

Procrastination and Anxiety

No one enjoys experiencing anxiety, and unfortunately for most medical school students, medical school produces a lot of it. You're always facing a ridiculous amount of information to learn with barely enough time to do so. Often there's a test looming. For many medical students, once school begins, anxiety can become a fixture of everyday life (if it wasn't present already). Some students may be in a constant state of worry and frustration, with much of their anxiety related to the studying they need to accomplish. Many are under the false impression that worrying is productive because it generates momentum and motivates them. What usually happens instead is that they keep putting off the work until the distress they feel causes them to take action to quell their anxiety. In other words, they procrastinate. It's as if they can take no action until their anxiety hits a near-breaking point.

Think of it as a nuclear fission reaction. Without a sufficient level of uranium inside the nuclear rods, no matter how much one tries, a nuclear fission reaction just won't happen. But once that critical mass of uranium is reached, the potential for fission reactions and nuclear power exists. In the procrastinator's case, before a critical mass of anxiety is reached, there is no potential for being productive, but after achieving that critical mass, the potential for productivity increases dramatically.

The first two years of medical school are typified by relentless test taking, so let's examine how a medical student can experience anxiety in relation to a testing cycle. Since many medical students are procrastinators, it is worthwhile to start by examining a procrastinator's level of anxiety versus time shown in figure 4.1.

In this simple example of anxiety versus time, the darker section displays a period of procrastination, while the lighter section shows a period of productivity. In examining the graph, you see that anxiety, while in the procrastination period, increases with time (here shown linearly, although it's hard to say what the exact relationship is). After the anxiety reaches a critical mass, the breaking point is achieved and studying commences. At this point, procrastination turns into productivity. It is also worth noting that the anxiety level decreases once productivity begins. The feeling of being productive provides a calming effect that counteracts the anxiety.

Anyone who has ever participated in competitive sports is familiar with this feeling. In high school, I competed in track. Before each race, I experienced anxiety, with the level increasing as the race time crept closer. My anxiety peaked when I was called to the starting line—fueled by a desire to do well combined with the knowledge that I was going to be in extreme pain. But once the race began, something funny always

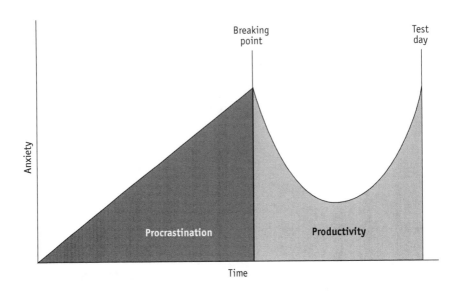

Figure 4.1 Procrastinator's study anxiety versus time

happened. My anxiety began to melt away almost as soon as I started running and completely disappeared by the time the race was done. It was as if the moments leading up to the race were more painful than the race itself, even though after the race I was so tired I could barely move. The act of racing vanquished the anxiety caused by having to race. The same is true when it comes to studying. The act of studying will help diminish the anxiety related to studying—though this simplified model does not take into account those suffering from a generalized level of anxiety or those whose anxiety is inflamed by other sources.

A major issue with procrastination is that until you reach the critical level of anxiety, you're left with the constant uncomfortable feeling of increasing anxiety. You need to ask yourself if the anxiety is absolutely necessary or, posed differently, if you can be just as successful while experiencing half the anxiety. Could you be successful without experiencing any anxiety at all? While eliminating all anxiety is difficult, nothing says that anxiety is absolutely necessary for productivity, so at least theoretically, it is possible to be productive without feeling anxiety. By the time you reach medical school, however, you have probably learned to associate worry and anxiety with productivity, and this is likely a behavior you've made no effort to change because it has been successful in the past and because it is the only way you've ever known. You may even believe you'll get nothing done unless you constantly think and worry about it. While this isn't true, some people have indeed convinced themselves that it is.

But is studying in a state of anxiety and procrastination the most efficient method for getting things done? This question more or less answers itself. Procrastination is almost by definition inefficient because it involves putting something off until the last minute, and when it involves studying, this usually means that you won't have time to study everything you might want to study before a big test. Even if you do eventually gain the motivation to study, you've handicapped yourself by not allowing sufficient time (see chapter 2, "Study Efficiency"). In essence, a study method that includes long periods of zero productivity and cramming is not nearly as efficient as is the practice of not cramming.

Notice in figure 4.1 that the level of anxiety rises again as test day approaches. This is a somewhat normal response for both procrastinators and nonprocrastinators and arises out of a fear of failure. Fear of failure doesn't necessarily mean that you're worried about receiving an F—in medical school, usually less than a score of 70 percent. Rather, it means that you're worried you won't achieve your desired score. For example, if your goal is to get a score above 90 percent, you're worried about scoring any lower; if your goal is 100 percent, you're almost certainly setting yourself up for failure and disappointment. Fear of failure is related to your perceived level of unpreparedness. The more unprepared you feel, the greater will be your fear of failure. A common problem with procrastination is that the pretest anxiety in procrastinators is often much higher than in those who don't procrastinate. As the test gets closer, the procrastinator's feeling of unpreparedness intensifies as he starts to realize that he may not have sufficient time to study everything he initially planned to study, and this inevitably leads to a sharp rise in pretest anxiety, anxiety the nonprocrastinator avoids.

So what happens after the test? It's logical to think that the anxiety related to the test would greatly diminish after the test has been taken. For some students this is true. Generally optimistic students will say something like, "Oh well, what's done is done. I can't do anything about it now. I think I did fine anyway." Other students will continue to experience test anxiety due to a combination of a lack of confidence and a fear of failure. You might overhear these students saying something like, "Oh, I hope I did all right" or, more commonly, "I think I failed that test." Sometimes these students will be angry with the test makers for creating "unfair" questions. A friend of mine in medical school once complained that he didn't feel confident about a test he had just taken. He told me that he certainly failed it and started to question whether medical school was really for him. A few weeks later I asked him how he scored on the test. As it turned out he did not even come close to failing. In fact, he did better than I did! I realized that his lack of self-confidence resulted in his irrational pessimism. I met many others like him in medical school, students who tended to focus on the few questions they didn't know, rather than on the multitude they knew. Even if they had difficulty with only five out of seventy questions, they focused on those five. Figure 4.2 shows a graphical depiction of this type of behavior.

Figure 4.2 depicts a constant level of anxiety that remains after the test has been taken, while students await the results. What specifically determines this level of constant anxiety is the intensity of the fear of failure, and this in turn is generally related to self-confidence. Obviously, a more confident student will experience less anxiety after taking the test than will a student lacking confidence. The anxiety felt while waiting for the test results has a limited time span. Some medical schools give grades quickly, while others take their time. The time for results may also vary from test to test, as some tests take longer to grade than do others. (Professors will often go over the distribution of answer choices for every question on a

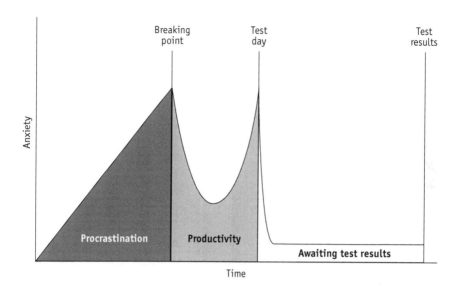

Figure 4.2 Procrastinator's study anxiety versus time, including posttest period

test and throw out bad questions.) After the grades have been given, the anxiety level can move in one of two directions:

- If the grade obtained was equal to or greater than what was desired, anxiety diminishes.

- If the grade obtained was lower than what was desired, anxiety increases.

In the first case, when the performance is on par with the goals, all the worrying and anxiety usually melt away. In some instances, students even experience jubilation. Chances are, this has happened to you at some point in your life since getting into medical school requires you to take count-less tests. But in the second case, when the performance does not meet the goals, disappointment will inevitably ensue, and this disappointment can be followed by a period of anger, particularly in those who feel their performance was due to circumstances that were out of their control. For example, one of my friends sometimes blamed a poor test result on a few

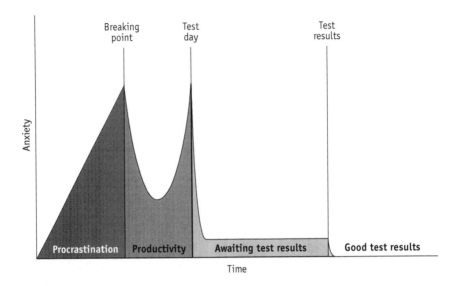

Figure 4.3 Procrastinator's study anxiety versus time with good test results

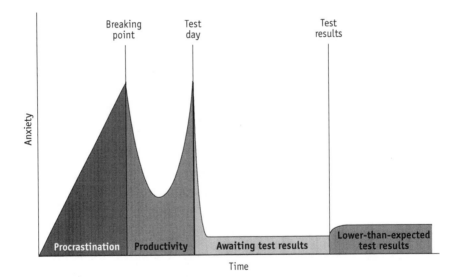

Figure 4.4 Procrastinator's study anxiety versus time with lower-than-expected test results

questions he thought were unfair. Regardless of whether or not you react in anger to disappointment, the end result is usually the same: anxiety rises. This is mainly due to the worry that your final grade won't be as high as you might want. This feeling can be a motivating factor to study harder and do better next time—but while this sounds positive, you need to use caution. The overwhelming desire to greatly increase your studying can be a potent source of anxiety. The two different situations are displayed in figures 4.3 and 4.4.

In figure 4.3, the student's level of anxiety diminishes rapidly when she obtains positive test results. In figure 4.4, the lower-than-expected test results cause her level of anxiety to rise.

Let's call the constant level of persisting anxiety the student's baseline anxiety—the amount of anxiety a student carries around at any given time between tests. Baseline anxiety is as much a function of the individual as it is of the test results. Most medical students tend toward worry and anxiety, but not all do. Some aren't even bothered by subpar test results. For the purpose of examining study anxiety, let's assume that the level of baseline anxiety is equal for all students, affected only by each student's perceived medical school performance. This level of baseline anxiety will tend to persist until the next test, at which point the testing cycle will start over and the level of baseline anxiety will have a chance to be adjusted.

The graphs on the previous page are for just one testing cycle and do not account for the presence of an initial baseline anxiety, but let's assume you're continually procrastinating. In that case, a picture of multiple testing cycles will look something like figure 4.5.

Figure 4.5 may initially appear confusing, so let's look closely. We're seeing the anxiety from one testing cycle superimposed on the next and the next. Since the pace of medical school is relentless, it is commonplace to have lectures on new material soon after a test, and since procrastinators don't start studying until close to test day, the cycles will necessarily overlap each other (unless there is a vacation period). The anxiety in anticipation of an upcoming test will build upon the baseline anxiety that was left over from the last test.

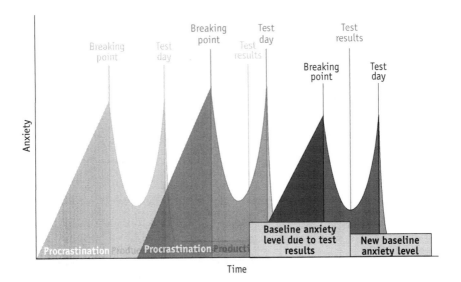

Figure 4.5 Procrastinator's study anxiety versus time with multiple superimposed testing cycles

Thus far, I have examined different periods of study anxiety as they relate to a test for a procrastinator, but as I mentioned earlier, anxiety is not a prerequisite for productivity. Rather, it is learned behavior that is associated with success. The point is, you don't have to worry all the time and experience high levels of anxiety to do well. You can do well without that pounding anxiety! So how do you get rid of your anxiety? While it is certainly possible to overcome study anxiety, this is a difficult habit to break. But that does not mean it's unbreakable. With enough effort and motivation, you can diminish study anxiety, and this in turn will lead you to a more efficient and happier existence.

First we must look at the initial area of study anxiety: the procrastination period. The main source of anxiety during this period is the uneasiness that comes with thinking about how much studying needs to get done. The procrastinator knows that he will spend the few days leading up to the exam in a constant state of study agony. He will think about the countless lectures he needs to review and how behind he has become. These thoughts can be so overwhelming that he forcibly drives them into his unconscious. In other words, whenever the thought of studying arises in the procrastinator, he actively suppresses it by doing something more enjoyable that takes his mind off studying. The key phrase here is *more enjoyable*; some procrastinators will clean their whole apartment and do their laundry simply to avoid studying—thus, normally tedious activities end up becoming preferable to studying. But while some procrastinators are relatively productive with their procrastination, most watch gratuitous amounts of TV.

How do we diminish the anxiety felt during the procrastination period? The short answer is to not procrastinate. This might sound simplistic, but it is true. But the question is, How can the procrastinator stop procrastinating?

Merriam-Webster defines *procrastinate* as "to put off intentionally the doing of something that should be done." But procrastinators don't put off everything they have to do. Most procrastinators of the world manage to find a way, for instance, to attend mandatory classes and to get up early for school or work. If they didn't, they wouldn't have graduated high school or couldn't maintain a job. Why do procrastinators procrastinate about some unenjoyable activities and not others? Working or attending school is a scheduled activity out of their control, one that cannot be put off. And since it can't be put off, procrastination isn't a factor. Compare this to studying for a test, an unscheduled activity that the procrastinator is able to put off. Herein lies the problem.

The Study Schedule

The tendency to procrastinate is rooted in unscheduled activities, so if you want to rid yourself of procrastination the key is to rid your life of unscheduled activities. This does not mean you must get rid of the activities themselves. Rather, you must schedule them. Create a study schedule, a daily set of goals you wish to accomplish in reference to studying. This need not be exhaustive or even written down; it just has to be followed.

A study schedule effectively gives you set goals for each day, and in accomplishing these, you are no longer procrastinating. When you are no longer procrastinating, you will no longer feel the study anxiety that goes along with that procrastination. This anxiety is essentially the feeling that you should always be studying during periods when you aren't. This feeling also creates an antagonistic relationship with any other activity. For example, the crammer and procrastinator will often say, "I shouldn't be watching TV/sleeping/doing something enjoyable; I should be studying," but because she has no study schedule and no set goals to accomplish, her feeling that more studying needs to be done will almost always be present. However, if you create and follow a study schedule, once you accomplish your daily goals, you'll feel no guilt when you stop. You'll enjoy the rest of your day guilt free.

How do you go about making a study schedule? A good study schedule will dictate the specific material you should study each day. Adhering to the schedule means that if you plan to study three specific lectures on Tuesday, you'll study just those lectures, no more and no less. If you plan to read two book chapters the Wednesday before Thursday's lecture, you'll read only those two chapters. The hard part is sticking to the schedule every day.

If you truly want to keep to your study schedule, you must observe the following two tenets:

- The study schedule is reasonable.
- The study schedule is written in stone.

Creating a reasonable study schedule is paramount to your fidelity toward it. Don't overwhelm yourself by choosing to study more material on a given day than you know you can comfortably absorb. If your Monday schedule is busy, don't schedule much studying for Monday. But if Thursday is wide open, study more that day. You're the only person who knows what you're capable of on any given day, but make sure to spread your studying out over a longer period of time than you might be accustomed to as you transition from procrastinating to not procrastinating.

Creating a reasonable schedule will enable you to make time for important activities. Say, for instance, you'd like to attend a sporting event on a Wednesday night but you have a test on Friday. The crammer could never attend the event—she'd be too busy cramming. But if you've created a study schedule and you have stuck to it, you can plan ahead and create enough free time to allow yourself to attend the event, despite the test! I once had a wedding to attend the weekend before a Monday test. I had to fly to Colorado for the wedding, but I made it there and back again and did fine on the test simply because I stuck to my study schedule.

Your study schedule is set in stone because there's no point in making a study schedule if you don't follow it. The key to a good schedule is creating a strong feeling of necessity and urgency related to keeping it. Need and urgency are powerful motivating factors that, when used properly, can overwhelm the drive to procrastinate. For example, you probably know procrastinators who can get to school at precisely 8:00 a.m. if they have a test to take that day—as I said earlier, procrastinators seldom put off activities that feel mandatory and out of their control. While it is hard to recreate that feeling of extreme need, if you understand that your schedule is set in stone, you'll be at least halfway there. Even though you may not always follow your schedule exactly, the desire to do so will help keep you on track.

By creating a reasonable study schedule and sticking to it, you'll effectively replace time spent procrastinating with time spent being productive. This newfound productivity will largely diminish the anxiety you normally feel during the procrastination period. A graphical representation of study anxiety versus time without procrastination is presented in figure 4.6.

This graph of one testing cycle starts with an arbitrary level of baseline anxiety. The baseline anxiety for a medical student is usually somewhere between an average person's and the level of a person with an anxiety disorder. The most obvious aspect of this graph is that the anxiety produced by the procrastination period has disappeared. The effective use of a study schedule has turned time spent procrastinating into time spent being productive. If a test is far enough away, the anxiety

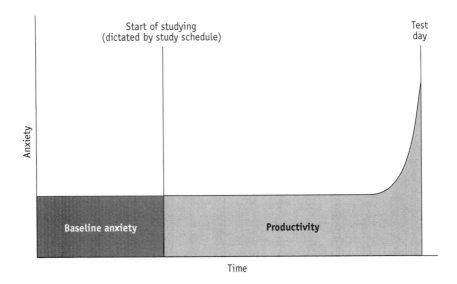

Figure 4.6 Nonprocrastinator's study anxiety versus time

you feel during the initial stages of productivity shouldn't increase much from the baseline level. Overall, the end result is that you will experience far less anxiety.

The level of anxiety starts to rise as test day approaches. Again, this is a normal response and can be attributed to your worry that you won't do well on the test—your fear of failure, which is rooted in your feeling unprepared. By following a study schedule and avoiding procrastination, you will have more time to study and should therefore feel more prepared. Unsurprisingly, the anxiety felt during this period will also be less.

Confidence and Anxiety

Confidence level and expectations can also contribute to worry—the higher your expectations, the greater the associated anxiety. If your goal is a perfect score and you'll settle for nothing less, you're bound to suffer greater anxiety than a fellow student who will be content with a score of 80 percent. This is not to say that you should set your goals low.

Rather, seek reasonable goals and you'll be far less anxious as you work to achieve them.

The more confident you are generally, the less anxiety you are likely to feel before a test, though it's important to note that overconfidence usually leads to unreasonable expectations and creates fertile ground for posttest disappointment and anxiety. Still, being underconfident is equally dangerous since feelings of inadequacy will often produce significant pretest anxiety. If you are truly underconfident and set abnormally low expectations, you'll be happy with your higher-than-expected test results and experience less anxiety after the test. Graphical depictions of the anxiety felt by an overconfident student (fig. 4.7), an underconfident student (fig. 4.8), and a student with a healthy level of confidence (fig. 4.9) will help shed light on the answer. (Again, these graphs focus on one testing cycle.)

Assuming that all students are following a strict study schedule, there should be no procrastination period or related anxiety. So let's start by examining the anxiety created during the productivity period. This period has two different phases: the constant phase and the upswing just before test day. The constant phase is the period in which you are studying hard but the test is not sufficiently close to produce anxiety. You know the test is soon, but right now you're concentrating on learning and memorizing the material. The anxiety felt during this phase of the productivity period arises from two different sources. One is your level of baseline study anxiety. (If multiple testing cycles were depicted there would no doubt be some overlap of the anxiety felt from the consecutive cycles. The leftover baseline anxiety from one cycle would add to the anxiety of the next cycle.) The other anxiety source is the knowledge that you'll spend most of your free time during the week before the test studying. I'm talking about the feeling you have when you wake up in the morning and know you have seven plus hours of studying ahead that must be done before you go to bed. In fact, this is the only real source of anxiety that the overconfident student feels during this period. The overconfident student has so much faith in his abilities, he knows beyond a shadow of a doubt that he will dominate the

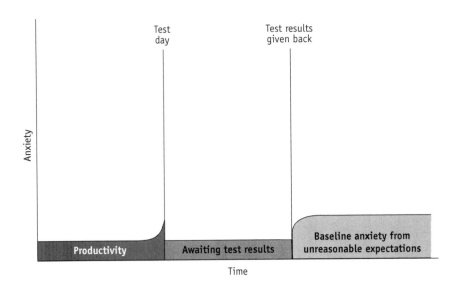

Figure 4.7 An overconfident student

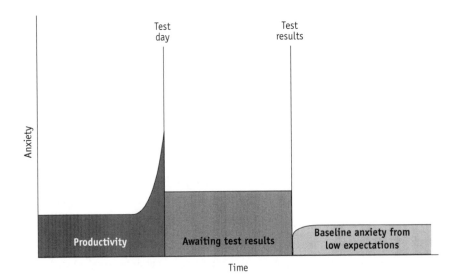

Figure 4.8 An underconfident student

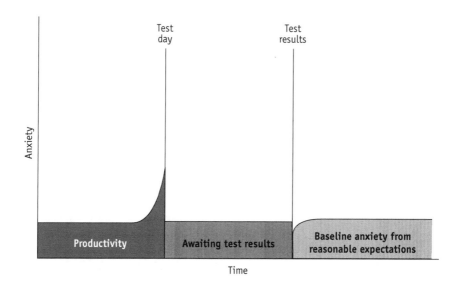

Figure 4.9 A student with a healthy level of confidence

next test. This overconfidence frequently leads to a superiority complex that years down the line may develop into a God complex. But the fact is, the overconfident student has little baseline study anxiety.

In stark contrast, the underconfident student's main source of anxiety stems from an abnormally high level of baseline study anxiety. She has little faith in her abilities (despite the fact that she got into medical school, which is arguably the hardest part of medical school), and she expects to do horribly on the test. This student likely possesses an inferiority complex. This is the student who in elementary school art class always exclaimed how bad her art looked so that everyone else had to compliment it. Like the overconfident student, the underconfident student experiences some anxiety about the excessive amount of studying she will need to do, but this is likely overshadowed by her high level of baseline study anxiety.

Finally, we come to the student who has a healthy level of confidence, the type of person who tends to be laid back, possessing a *qué será, será* attitude. This student has no illusions about what he is capable of achieving. Whether he usually receives test grades in the high 90s or low 70s, he has no false expectations about his abilities and thus has a relatively low baseline anxiety, lower than the underconfident student's but higher than the overconfident student's. Of course, even the healthily confident student isn't immune from the anxiety related to the excessive amounts of studying medical students are required to do, but realistic expectations have led to a reasonable baseline anxiety level.

Feeling some anxiety right before a test as the fear of failure starts to enter the picture is only natural for all students. This is shown on figures 4.7 through 4.9 as the upswing period that occurs immediately before the test. Again, this fear of failure is based on the thought of being unprepared and is normally a combination of the feelings you haven't studied enough and that the test will be unreasonably hard. The former sentiment is often more rational than the latter, although both tend toward the irrational. The overconfident student feels that he knows everything there is to know and that he won't find a question on the test that he can't answer correctly. The fear of failure is markedly diminished or even absent in the overconfident student, so the anxiety level during the upswing period is barely noticeable. For the underconfident student, the situation is precisely the opposite. She knows that the next test will be impossible and that failure is imminent despite all the studying she has done, so the fear of failure is very real and thus the anxiety associated with the upswing period is significant. The healthily confident student who occupies the middle ground between the other two students believes he has studied sufficiently to achieve the desired grade. He may feel some uncertainty, but he is reasonably certain things will work out in the end.

Moving past the productivity period, you're in test-taking limbo, the period when you've taken the exam but not yet received the results. Feelings of unpreparedness disappear along with the worry associated with studying excessively. Still, most students experience some residual anxiety in this immediate posttest phase because the fear of failure is still very much alive. This period is often typified by the reoccurring thought, *I hope I did well*, which often occurs without warning and is enough to make you stop whatever you are doing, at least for a few seconds. You might find yourself staring off into space between bites of a sandwich or zoning out during the ride to school as the fear of failure reenters your mind. The overconfident student will have this thought least often because he knows he did well. Some of his peers may have gotten different answers, but the overconfident student has no problem showing others the errors of their ways. In the few instances when everyone chose a different answer, the overconfident student is convinced that those questions were poorly written and will certainly be thrown out.

At the other end of the spectrum, the underconfident student experiences many intrusively pessimistic thoughts after the test and tends to focus on the few questions that she was unsure about rather than the multitude of questions she knew. When asked about the answer she gave for a specific test question, this student will almost surely respond by saying something along these lines: "I don't know. I thought it was B, but I'm probably wrong. I'm usually wrong. Don't listen to me."

As always, the healthily confident student resides in an area between these two extremes, feeling confident about the questions he probably got right and confident that he probably answered some questions wrong, thus creating a realistic representation of the grade he is likely to receive. The healthily confident student may actually be able to predict his score. Since the healthily confident student more or less knows the grade he is going to get on the test, he usually won't experience much anxiety while waiting for the results. (The exception, of course, is the healthily confident student who thinks he has failed—the difference between his thought and the underconfident student's fear is that he probably did fail.) The healthily confident student may feel some anxiety related to the questions he knows he answered incorrectly, but the anxiety from this source is usually minimal.

Often when test results are finally given out, a small commotion ensues. It usually starts with someone yelling, "Grades are up!" followed by a mad rush to find a computer. Everything grows silent as all students anxiously check their grades at the same time. The reactions of our three sample students would probably proceed as follows:

- *The underconfident student:* "Oh wow! I can't believe it. I was sure I failed that test! This is great. I'm so happy! This is going to be such a good weekend."

- *The healthily confident student:* "Yup, that's what I thought I was going to get. I wonder what I'm going to buy today for lunch. Maybe I'll get that spicy buffalo wrap. That was really tasty last time I got it. Yeah, I think I'll definitely get the spicy buffalo wrap."

- *The overconfident student:* "What! There must be something wrong with the computer—let me log in again and recheck it. Still the same grade? No way. I got just about every question right. They must have entered the grade incorrectly. They probably didn't throw out those horrible questions. It's not my fault that they make bad questions. They're the ones who should suffer from it, not me. I hate this school!"

As expected, the underconfident student did much better than she thought she would, and now that she has her test grade back, she can see how inaccurate her predictions were. Jubilation usually ensues, and baseline anxiety plummets. Could the underconfident student's confidence level possibly rise? Absolutely, but it would be unrealistic to think that an underconfident student will instantaneously transform into an overconfident one. Indeed, the underconfident student's confidence level will probably approach that of the healthily confident student for the next test, though the underconfident student might remain underconfident.

The story of the overconfident student is quite different. Unsurprisingly, his disappointment and frustration are vividly evident. The normal response of the overconfident student is to immediately rationalize, blaming others for his errors and often blaming the test itself, claiming that it was poorly written. These rationalizations are an unconscious attempt by the overconfident student to maintain his overconfidence, and because the overconfident student usually is also stubborn, his confidence level likely will remain abnormally high. However, the overconfident student might begin to see that he has legitimately made some mistakes; the more often he is disappointed in this manner, the more likely his confidence level will begin to approach a healthy level. Either way, the overconfident student will feel his performance was unacceptable and that he must do much better on the next test. This might result in his significantly ramping up his studying, and as a result his baseline anxiety may rise dramatically—so much so, in fact, that he might give up doing anything enjoyable.

The healthily confident student with realistic expectations about performance will likely not be surprised by the test results. Indeed, so unshaken is this student, the thought of the test grade occupies little more than a few seconds in his mind—test grades just aren't a big deal, and his baseline anxiety neither rises nor falls.

So why doesn't the baseline anxiety of the healthily confident student disappear altogether? The answer is that every medical student experiences some level of baseline anxiety (even the healthily confident ones who do well). Medical school means you'll have many things to do without enough time to do all of them, and this fact creates unrelenting time pressure. The average medical student is likely to struggle to accomplish everything, and it is hard for even the most calm and confident medical students to completely rid themselves of anxiety. It's best simply to know you won't rid yourself of anxiety altogether.

Still, it's easy to see which confidence level is preferable. The under-confident student experiences more anxiety before the test, the overconfident student experiences more afterward, and the healthily confident student experiences the least overall anxiety. Does this mean the healthily confident student will perform less well than the overconfident student? Not at all. It's important to remember that anxiety is not a prerequisite for performing well. Rather, it is a learned behavior that some have always associated with doing well. The healthily confident student may be healthily confident his studying will usually earn him grades in the mid-90s, or he might be healthily confident his preparation will produce a grade in the mid-70s. Whether this student is earning high grades or low grades, the point is he has realistic expectations based on his abilities and time commitment to studying. Through consistency and acceptance, the healthily confident student will experience less overall anxiety.

How to Be Healthily Confident

How can you develop a healthy level of confidence? Perhaps a better way to ask this question is, How can you create realistic expectations? At the start of medical school, when you are facing the unknown, creating realistic expectations will be difficult. Before the first test, it is normal to worry that you haven't studied enough or that the questions may be too hard. But as you take more tests and fine-tune your study skills, you'll begin to have a much better idea of what you are capable of achieving. This creates fertile ground for realistic expectations, and as the months pass and you take more and more tests, your expectations will become more realistic, the process will seem old hat, and as a result you'll experience less anxiety.

Once you have some idea of your expected test results (based on your test-taking capabilities and time commitment to studying), you can take one of two routes: You can accept your situation or you can be bothered by it. If you accept your test-taking abilities and are generally content with your performance, you'll have achieved a healthy level of confidence. The consistency of your test-taking performance and contentedness related to it will greatly diminish the anxiety normally associated with studying and test taking. On the other hand, if you are continually unhappy with your test grades, you'll experience a great deal of anxiety. This is not to say you shouldn't push yourself to do your very best, but there is a difference between trying to do your best and setting up unrealistic expectations. As you move deeper into medical school, you'll have a better idea of how much studying you need to do to obtain a certain grade. Being content with your performance is key. If you truly desire to earn a higher grade, you'll have to study more. (Take caution—the relationship between studying and grades is not linear—see chapter 3, "Diminishing Returns.") Whatever grade you strive to achieve, your goal is to create realistic expectations about the studying required to get there and to be content with the path you have chosen to take.

Summary

The anxiety associated with studying and test taking in medical school will always be present—medical school is an inherently stressful undertaking that often requires gratuitous amounts of studying. But study anxiety is not a prerequisite to performing well on a test, and you can greatly diminish the anxiety you experience. The more you can control your anxiety, the better you'll feel and the happier you will become. The best way to avoid study anxiety is to avoid procrastination by creating and following a reasonable study schedule. In addition, creating realistic expectations of your test-taking capabilities is key.

This chapter has taken you on a journey through the realm of study anxiety as we examined the many facets of the testing cycle and learned ways to overcome the anxiety associated with each part. And although following a study schedule may seem simple enough it will not be easy to achieve, but in achieving it, you'll discover the gratification of reduced anxiety.

5 | Studying for the USMLE
Step 1: End of the Second Year

You can hardly believe that the end of your second year of medical school is rapidly approaching. You're excited to think that only a few more lectures remain between you and your final class test. It has been a long road, and you're tired of sitting in class for hours on end. You're tired of making sure that you memorize every single detail of every single lecture slide. You're tired of taking meticulous notes. You will welcome the change to third year, when you will finally be able to gain some real-life clinical experience. Instead of just reading and hearing about medicine, you will actually experience it. The last day of class comes and goes but your celebration is short-lived, for one last hurdle remains between you and your third-year clinical clerkships (also known as rotations). It just so happens that this hurdle is colossal, known to all as the USMLE (United States Medical Licensing Examination) Step 1.

You knew when you started medical school that eventually you would have to take this test, but back then you barely thought about it, much less worried about it. As time passed, once in a while during lectures you heard professors mention it: "You don't need to know this right now, but you'll probably want to know it for Step 1." Every time they said that, your anxiety rose ever so slightly, and with each passing week, the thought of the test became more real. As happens in medical school, sometimes you came across a tidbit of medical knowledge you once knew but had since forgotten. This only raised your level of anxiety since you knew that at some point in the future, you would have to review this forgotten knowledge. You knew you'd have to polish rusty areas and fill knowledge gaps. *But not yet,* you would think. *The test isn't for a while.* That thought was usually enough to send your anxiety about the test burrowing back into the far reaches of your subconscious. Today, as you reach the end of your second year, "not yet" is replaced with "now."

The USMLE Step 1 is an intimidating test for any second-year medical student. It incorporates everything you learned during the first two years, as well as everything that you were supposed to learn but didn't. Medical schools almost expect students to forget some of the knowledge they learned over the two years due to the sheer number of details. For example, at some point, all medical students probably have a decent knowledge of the brachial plexus, but ask students details about the brachial plexus a year after they learned it and chances are they won't remember much about it. Therefore, medical schools give second-year students some time (usually one to two months, sometimes longer) to study for and take the USMLE Step 1. A second-year medical student must pass the Step 1 to continue on to the third year. Step 1 is, in essence, the SAT of medical school. If you want to secure a spot in a competitive residency, you'll need to do well.

How should a medical student go about studying for this test? As you might guess, studying for Step 1 starts with learning the material in class. Although this material is sometimes overly detailed or not detailed enough, it does provide the foundation for board review. The average medical student needs two years of near-constant studying to learn all the material covered in Step 1. It would be nearly impossible for anyone to learn everything from scratch in the two-month study period leading up to the exam. Even if you've forgotten many of the details you learned by the time Step 1 studying starts, you should have retained the major concepts and details on most topics, and retaining this knowledge makes relearning the microdetails easier. If you've forgotten everything about a subject, you'll need to exert that much more effort to get back up to speed. Indeed, the best way to prepare for Step 1 during the first two years of medical school is simply to learn and retain the information presented in class as best you can (see chapter 2, "Study Efficiency").

The next and possibly most important step toward studying for Step 1 is to create a reasonable study schedule. You'll have a great deal of material to review for this test, and without some sort of day-to-day road map for reviewing it, you can easily become lost. Ideally, like a class study schedule, your Step 1 study schedule should dictate what you will study each day. This does not mean that you must plan every hour precisely; rather, you should have a general idea of the specific topics you will study each day and how many practice questions you want to answer each day. Like studying for a class test, your study schedule must be reasonable. Overtaxing yourself early on could lead to disaster. Creating a reasonable study schedule will allow you to keep on task while minimizing the chance of burnout. And very simply, a reasonable study schedule is one that you can realistically follow. If you believe you are capable of studying twelve hours a day, every day, your study schedule could contain twelve-hour days. If, on the other hand, you know you cannot possibly study for that many hours, your study schedule should contain no twelve-hour days.

The best way to create a reasonable study schedule is to find an upperclass student who did well on Step 1 and copy that student's study schedule. There is no reason to reinvent the wheel and no shame in trying to replicate someone else's good results. Of course, you'll want to edit the schedule to fit your specific needs. For example, you'll probably want to spend less time on topics you're confident about and more time on topics you're unsure of. Also, make sure the schedule you copy is reasonable, or edit it to make it so. Some schedules may require you to study during the school year. But if you study for Step 1 during the school year (not necessary for most people), you need to make sure that the Step 1 schedule is reasonable and compatible with your class and class study schedules.

Once you've drawn up a reasonable study schedule, the next step is to obtain the proper review materials. Almost every student uses some combination of review books and question banks to prepare for Step 1. Review books are great for providing high-yield material in a concise, intelligible manner, and a good question bank is powerful study material that can be worth its weight in gold. Doing practice questions is a perfect way to test and augment your knowledge while you become familiar with the format of the test. Review books and question banks are equally important in preparing for the Step 1, and just about every study schedule will dictate the use of both.

The issue now becomes finding the best review book or question bank among the multitude of choices. Some review materials are clearly better than others, and picking the right ones is paramount. Again, the best approach is to ask upperclass students which materials they found most helpful. Usually you'll get a consensus on this. A common pitfall is buying more review materials than you could ever use. Finding a few good review books is more efficient than purchasing everything you find and wading through the pages of each to find the section worth reading. Most students ultimately use two or three review books.

Some students also use auxiliary materials such as flash cards. Flash cards can be a great way to learn topics that require a lot of memorization, though keeping track of all the cards and deciding which you know well enough to skip and which you need to review more often can be a challenge.

A great solution to this problem is to create an electronic deck. Many computer programs are available that can track which cards should be reviewed more often and which should be reviewed less often. (This kind of study is known as spaced repetition learning.) If you are familiar with the material on a card, you'll score it so that it shows up less frequently than those with which you're not as familiar. The program will remember your score, and the cards you don't know as well will show up more often—until you have learned that material. The program can set a schedule that lets you know how many cards you need to review each day.

One downside to this method is that for it to be maximally effective, you'll need to review the flash cards every day; if you miss a day, the cards scheduled for that day will be added to the next day's scheduled cards, and as a result, if you miss a few days in a row, the number of flash cards you must review can easily become daunting and you might then quit using them. Another downside is that you will need to manually enter every flash card into the program. (This will, however, help you learn the material.) I can well imagine that in the future, review books will also be offered in flash card form. Flash cards were the main component of my personal study method and proved to be one of the most efficient ways to memorize a large body of facts. In total, I had over nine thousand cards, composed of facts pulled from a few prominent review books.

Never use your notes from class as your main study material. While class notes can be great for reviewing central concepts not explained well in review books, they will usually be overly detailed and ineffective at summarizing large amounts of information. Class notes help you study for class tests, while Step 1 review books were created to help you study for Step 1. It is a mistake not to take advantage of the hard work the review book creators put into distilling the mass of information.

After creating a reasonable study schedule and acquiring most of the study materials you need, you'll have to begin studying. Getting up every morning knowing you have to study for most of the day isn't easy, and it can be even harder if you think about all the studying you'll be doing over the next several weeks. Step 1 studying can wear down even the most resilient.

The ultimate goal is to keep faithful to your study schedule and to take the test when planned, and to do this most easily, you need to take life one day at a time. You need a reasonable schedule if you're going to take care of your mental health while you study. If you know you need to take a day off every once in a while to remain truly committed to your schedule, you should include days off in that schedule. If you know you need to work out every day to stay sane, factor in your workout time as well. A night out with friends every once in a while might not hurt either. Instead of thinking, *I should be studying*, think, *Going out tonight will let my mind recover and relax so that tomorrow I will be more focused.*

Not every medical student studies for the boards every waking hour of every day. While some do, many treat Step 1 studying as a nine-to-five job. You might want to create a schedule that includes a stop time of 5:00 p.m. each day to help you stick to your schedule and stay sane. A maxim that is just as true for Step 1 studying as it was for class test studying is that you should never study while tired. Getting up at 5:00 a.m. to study might sound like a good idea, but if it causes you to fall asleep and lose concentration by noon, it's a bad idea. Studying while tired is always inefficient and should be avoided at all costs.

Another bad habit some students tend to have is to keep pushing their test date back to "get in more studying." Ideally, you'll want to take the Step 1 test at the point of maximum knowledge retention. In other words, take the test when the amount of knowledge you have is greatest. This will be affected by two factors: the amount of knowledge you're learning every day and the amount of knowledge you're forgetting every day. Pushing back your test date can be a bad idea because the further you push it back, the less you'll remember about what you studied early on (unless your study schedule calls for constant review of all subjects). One of three possible scenarios will ensue:

- If the material you studied at the end was higher yield than what you studied at the beginning, you could earn a higher score.
- If the material you studied at the end was lower yield than what you studied at the beginning, you could earn a lower score.
- If the material you studied at the end was the same yield as what you studied at the beginning, you could earn the same score.

It thus makes logical sense to push back your test date if the material you studied at the end is higher yield than what you studied at the beginning. Otherwise your score will probably be the same as or possibly even lower than it might have been had you taken the test when originally planned. A lot of medical students end up pushing back their test date to spend more time focusing on nitpicky details. Students who do this run the serious risk of learning a few microdetails while forgetting higher-yield material. They might not only decrease their score but also torture themselves by studying for an even longer period of time! This isn't to say no one should ever push back the test date. If something unfortunate happens in your personal life and forces you to take a break from studying, pushing back the date makes sense.

The reason most medical students push back their test date is the anxiety they feel about not being ready. They usually feel this way toward the beginning of the study schedule, but how can they feel ready when they've just begun to study? When every day of your life is leading up to a single event, it is only natural to experience some anxiety about it. Worries about the test questions' difficulty or one's level of preparation are common. Doubt and anxiety may begin to develop concerning the strength of your study schedule, but relieving this anxiety by pushing back the test date may not be the wisest course of action. Usually students go this route because of emotion rather than logic. You need to have supreme confidence in your study schedule and continually remind yourself that it has worked for others in the past and that there is no reason it won't work for you. Of course, you can always modify your schedule, but doubting it is unproductive.

Other students push back their test date because they have procrastinated and not stuck to their study schedule. Creating a reasonable study schedule is paramount in eliminating the problem of procrastination. Again, if you find the schedule you have created too intense, you should edit it or find another schedule that better suits your needs.

The final step of this whole process is to actually take the test. Many say that getting a good night's sleep the night before the test is important, and I don't think anyone would disagree. The only problem is that despite measures you take to relax, your anxiety level may increase as test day approaches, and it can reach a maximum point the night before the exam. This can make sleeping a real challenge. The night before I took my test, I was so wired I could barely sleep. The more I wanted to sleep, the less I was able to. I nervously paced around my apartment, gulped down warm milk, and read books, desperately trying anything I could (short of taking medication) to fall asleep. I felt like I was sabotaging myself and counteracting all my months of hard work. Finally, like a toddler, I ran out of steam and around 3:45 a.m. I fell asleep. I was worried that the few hours of sleep I got wouldn't be enough and that I might end up taking a nap during the test. To my surprise, however, I never for a moment felt sleepy during the test. The thought that I was actually taking the Step 1 test provided enough adrenaline for me to make it through the day.

So don't worry too much if you're unable to get a full night's rest before the exam. Your nerves will surely carry you through. One small measure you can take to help decrease your pretest anxiety is to go to the testing center a few days before the test to familiarize yourself with how to get there. Also, set multiple alarm clocks for the morning of the test and make sure you have the required documents and some snacks to bring along. (On test day I even took an extra pair of underwear with me, though thankfully I didn't find a reason to use them.)

The test is potentially eight hours long if you take the full hour for each of the seven sections and use your full one-hour break time (forty-five minutes if you don't skip the tutorial). You can elect to take a break between sections if you desire, as long as the total cumulative break time isn't over one hour. No one needs to power through the whole test in one sitting, and I encourage you to make frequent use of your break time to get up, stretch, and refocus. A few short breaks can go a long way. Since the test is long and everyone just wants to be done with it, some students have the tendency to blow off the last section. Faltering at the end because you are impatient is foolish. Take care on the final section. Slow down and give every question its appropriate focus, and you're bound to succeed.

Summary

The Step 1 is a daunting exam, but if you prepare for it properly, you shouldn't have any problems doing well on it. The first and most important step is to be diligent during the first two years of medical school and make every effort to learn the material in class. Second, create a study schedule based on a successful upperclass student's, and modify it for your own needs, making sure it is reasonable. This will help keep you on track and provide a road map to success. Next, obtain the best review materials based on a consensus of students who have already taken the exam. Again, try not to push your test date back unless it is for a very good reason. Last, make sure you take breaks during the exam and don't simply rush to finish.

6 | Transition to the Third Year

The loud, familiar beep of your alarm clock pierces the air and you welcome it like an old enemy. But there's no time to be tired this morning. This is a momentous day—the first day of your third year, the day that seemed infinitely far away while you were in the depths of your Step 1 studying. You remember wishing you could press a button like the one on your DVD player and fast-forward time or that you could enter some sort of functional hibernation. Anything would have been better than studying for that test all damn day. Thankfully, those days are now done. Step 1 is in your past. Enough reminiscing. There's no point in reliving the depression of your Step 1 studying days.

Getting ready in the morning knowing that you don't have a full anxiety-ridden day of Step 1 studying ahead of you feels great. There, you did it again! Despite your best efforts, you cannot erase the memory of that test. The days of wearing jeans and T-shirts are gone. You rummage through your closet, searching for your Sunday best. You suddenly realize you own just three dress shirts and two ties. What's more, you don't want to wear any of the shirts because the necks are too small. You don't have enough dress clothes to last through the week. As you grab your white coat, you make a mental note to go shopping this weekend. The pockets of your coat are still filled with whatever you left in there before you started studying for Step 1. Again? As you open the door to leave your apartment, you glance toward your backpack slumped in the corner of the room. It's then you realize that this is the first day you don't need your backpack to go to school. Wow.

Being late for third-year orientation at the hospital is absolutely the last thing you would ever want to do. So, being a typical medical student, you leave your apartment early, giving yourself approximately twice the amount of time it should take to get there. As it turns out, as you pull into the visitors' parking lot twenty-five minutes early, you realize you left yourself triple the time. But you are okay with this since the thought of struggling to find a parking spot or running exasperated through the unfamiliar hospital corridors makes you shudder. Once inside, after getting lost a couple of times, you finally manage to find where you are supposed to be. Again you've make the mistake of thinking that you are going to be the first one there. Half the class is already sitting down, and they're all vigorously reading the orientation material. It's nice to see some familiar faces and not so nice to see others. The conversation quickly collapses into Step 1 chatter, and as much as you don't want to talk about it anymore, you can't help yourself.

As the clock ticks to 8:00 a.m., one of your professors moves toward the front of the room. A wave of silence quickly passes over the gathered crowd and the professor enthusiastically says, "Welcome to third year!" A nervous smile crosses your face. You have no idea what to expect in the weeks ahead, but whatever it is, it has to be better than second year.

For almost everyone, the third year of medical school is a welcome change from the second year. The days of attending lectures for hours on end and forcing yourself to memorize every single lecture slide are finally over. Now if a professor wants to discuss his research, you don't have to listen and record every detail for fear that something he says might show up on an exam. In fact, if you're so inclined, you don't have to listen at all (although it is never a bad idea to feign interest).

Comparing any activity to the second year is not a fair contest; almost anything else would come out on top if you were asked, "What would you rather do?" But the third year of medical school has its own merits as well. Just about all of us who decide to enter medical school do so because we eventually want to practice medicine. This drive to practice medicine is usually rooted in the desire to help sick people in need and the good feeling that comes along with doing so. Alas, upon entering medical school, we do not encounter sick people in need; rather, we are bombarded by books, lectures, and tests. Obviously, physicians must possess a large and deep foundation of clinical knowledge, and there is so much to know. And during the first two years of medical school, that foundation is being built. Unfortunately, our altruistic sentiments must be bottled up and stored away during the first two years. For most of us, they remain a motivating factor and help us suffer through the days of endless studying. "It will all be worth it when I become a doctor" becomes the oft-repeated mantra, and medical students become masters of delayed gratification.

As a third-year student, you'll finally find yourself immersed in the clinical world of medicine. Being on your feet and interacting with patients rather than sitting on your butt all day studying produces a kind of joy. Actually seeing the diseases you've studied and helping with a patient's care feels good. Those bottled-up sentiments can be released. This is what most medical students signed up for, and the third year may be the first time you find yourself doing something you actually want to do on a daily basis. (Note: Some schools offer a fair amount of clinical experience during the first two years, but usually just one or two afternoons a week, and most students see these clinical forays either as a break or a distraction from studying, especially near exam times.)

It's not hard to guess what happens when someone begins to do something he has wanted to do every day for two years. He becomes happier. And for many medical students, this is the case. On average, medical students are much happier during the third year than they were in the second year. Of course, happiness levels depend somewhat on the clinical rotation. For example, if a student detests surgery, she probably won't be happy while on surgery rotation, or if a rotation requires a medical student do a lot of scut work during ungodly hours of the day, he might end up hating his life. But aside from disliked rotations, the third year of medical school is more enjoyable than the second year.

I have to note that there are exceptions to this generalization. Some students prefer the second year. These are the students who reap greater enjoyment from studying and test taking than from actually interacting with other human beings in a clinical environment. This academic type of student just happens to love school, and it's not uncommon for these students to already have pursued multiple masters degrees or even a doctorate. These people feel more comfortable in the company of books and data than in the company of patients and may end up becoming research doctors, and certainly we need research physicians.

Then there are those students who don't like the third year any more than they liked the second year, students who see the third year as just another unhappy chapter on the road to physicianship. This sentiment might arise from being stuck in an unpleasant rotation, but some students cannot find a rotation they enjoy. This is a bad sign and may mean they do not like medicine and went to school because they thought they would like it, because they were forced by pushy parents, or because they wanted to become a doctor because of the associated lifestyle. The first case is unfortunate since these students have already invested heavily in their education—two years of their lives and tens of thousands of dollars—and stopping now would be a waste, so they carry on, hoping eventually to find a rotation they can enjoy. The second case is almost equally as unfortunate because these students never had a choice. Perhaps they would be happier as a teacher or firefighter, but sadly, their parents don't see it that way. As for students who went into medicine because of the lifestyle, they view the third year as simply another obstacle in the path toward obtaining a medical degree. These students dream of a high-paying, stable, prestigious job that will allow them to purchase the material things they have always desired, and they're forever fantasizing about fast-forwarding through medical school and residency. The problem is that despite all the material gains they will eventually accrue, it's unlikely they'll ever be happy. Being a physician is time demanding—but this is a subject that calls for its own book. Suffice it to say that every medical school class has at least a handful of students who fall into these categories, but it's important not to let others' unhappiness color your own relief and joy.

The third year is radically different from the second year, but although it is exciting, at the start it is also scary. Every second-year medical student asks, "What's third year like?" And the simple answer is, the third year is variable. One big difference between the second and third years is that during the second year, everyone learns everything at the same time. If the subject taught in class is the physiology of the heart, everyone is thinking, reading, and talking about physiology of the heart. Since it would be almost impossible to put a whole third-year class in one rotation at the same time, the class is split up into different rotations. By the end of the third year, everyone will have done the same required rotations, but they'll have done them at different times. Common third-year rotations include surgery, internal medicine, psychiatry, pediatrics, obstetrics and gynecology, neurology, and family medicine. Of course, each medical school is slightly different, but most schools offer the previously mentioned clerkships as required entities.

What this means is that come the start of the third year, one student could be on a psychiatry rotation while another could be on a surgery rotation. The student on the surgery rotation might arrive at the hospital at 5:00 a.m. to start rounding on their patients and not leave until 7:00 p.m., while the student on the psychiatry rotation may get to the psych unit at 8:00 a.m. and leave by noon every day. The surgery student might also work most weekends, while the psychiatry student might work none.

Eventually, students switch rotations, and at some point the student who was on the surgery rotation will be on a psychiatry rotation and vice versa. It might seem, then, that in the end everything evens out, but the truth is that it doesn't always work this way. For example, the student formerly on the surgery rotation may have a team of psychiatric residents and attending physicians who make him work much longer hours than his peer had to. They may even have the student come in on weekends. It's also possible that the student who started on the psychiatry rotation may have a team of surgery residents and attendings who are relaxed and require half the amount of time his peer had to work. It's unfair, but that's the way it is.

Not knowing exactly what to expect from the third year can arouse anxiety. A good way to find out more about a specific rotation is to question a student who has already completed it. She can often provide valuable advice—for instance, about what a certain attending wants to see in notes or something to avoid doing because it will provoke the attending physician's anger. Unfortunately, what one student says about a rotation won't always decrease the anxiety associated with your starting it, especially if your fellow student describes the rotation as taxing. But remember that someone else's likes and dislikes may be different from yours, and your experience of someone's "unpleasant" rotation could just as easily be great. For example, a student might describe his pediatric rotation as miserable because he doesn't like children and didn't get along with his attendings and residents. After hearing his descriptions, you might approach your pediatric rotation expecting the worst only to find that you get along with your medical team and love taking care of children. In other words, take your fellow students' advice with a giant grain of salt and avoid passing judgment on a rotation until you have experienced it for yourself.

Summary

Each medical student has a unique third-year experience. Medical schools try their best to make sure that rotations are fair and that every student has a similar experience, but it is impossible to control for every variable. With a multitude of attending physicians and residents, you'll face a multitude of personalities. Some may be easygoing and nice, while others may be stern and less than pleasant. A workaholic may work insane hours, but another physician might be more laid back and reasonable. Some students will have a harder third-year experience than will others. This is a fact of medical school life. But difficulties aside, most students end up liking the third year a whole lot more than the second year. You should approach every rotation with a positive outlook and not let your peers' opinions paint your rose-colored glasses black.

7 | Clerkships

You find yourself chuckling at the sight of your friend slipping off his barstool. The sight becomes even funnier as he grabs your other friend for balance. The looks on their faces are priceless as they fall together, one on top of the other. You manage to glance at your watch only to notice that it is 7:03 a.m. This sobering detail quickly pulls you out of your daydream about last weekend. It's Monday morning, and it's earlier than you want to be awake. You remember the days when you thought that waking up at 7:00 was early, never mind already being somewhere by 7. Anyway, there's a reason you are at the hospital so early: you have a job to do. Rounds don't start until 8:00, which means you have slightly less than an hour to see all your patients and write up notes on them. It's important to do a good job today because this is the first time you are working with this medical team, and first impressions are everything.

It's the third week of your pediatrics rotation and you're starting to feel a bit more comfortable. You remember how awkward doing rounds and writing notes was during your first rotation at the beginning of the year. You remember being so worried about the right questions to ask, what to write down, what not to write down. But by now you've written so many notes, writing is no longer a big deal. Although you didn't know that much pediatric medicine when you started, you feel that your fund of knowledge has grown dramatically over the past few weeks. All your diligent studying has been paying off. All in all, you're confident this Monday morning.

It's all fairly routine by now: Do a quick H&P (history and physical exam), grab the patient's chart, look at the labs, look at the progress notes, talk to the nurse, record the vitals, and then write a perfect SOAP note (a subjective, objective, assessment, plan note, a common progress note style that every third-year medical student is familiar with). Although you are not exactly sure what the plan for your patient should be, you have a good idea based on what you've seen during the past few weeks, what the residents have said, and what you have read. The next hour flies by as you work vigorously. Comparing the movement of time this year to the snail's pace of last year's lectures brings a smile to your face. You are happy to be done with that part of your education.

After signing your name on the last note, you come up for air and begin to look for the attending. Alas, she is nowhere in sight, and that's when you remember that this attending is known for arriving half an hour late every day. You wish you had remembered that fact last night when you were setting your alarm, but then you recall a conversation you had with another medical student who said that the one day he came in later to rounds, the attending was early, and she yelled at him for being late. *Oh well. It's 8:05 now, so I guess I'll just hang out for the next twenty-five minutes*, you think and allow yourself to look around and take in your surroundings. The dimly lit hospital floor is an amalgamation of cartoon posters, worn paint, and tired people. One resident's face droops with sleepiness, while another's is energetically smiling. You see one of your friends on the other side of the hall perched over his patient's chart and decide to mosey on over to bother him for a while. As it turns out, he is just putting the finishing touches on his last note and waiting for his attending. While talking, you manage to keep one eye out for the attending, prepared to start work at a moment's notice, like a soldier waiting to be called into action.

Just then, out of the corner of your eye, you see an object moving down the hallway at a much faster pace than anything around it. It looks almost like a speed-walking race with just one participant. Ah yes, there she is. You take another glance at your watch: 8:43, which means your attending is forty-three minutes late. She was probably just busy with something else, and you'd never even think of mentioning her tardiness; doing so would create a world of trouble.

"Okay, who do we have first?" she asks in an exasperated voice. You look into your friend's eyes and see he wants to speak first, so you let him. He takes out his progress note and presents his patient to the attending. As he systematically covers all aspects of his patient's status, she listens attentively, and when your friend is finished, he looks worriedly confident. He seems confident because that is what he is supposed to be and worried because this attending has a no-nonsense reputation. After the attending nods approval, your friend's face flushes with pride, but his beaming countenance suddenly expresses dread as the attending's eyes focus and he realizes the onslaught is about to begin. She bombards him with questions shot like cannonballs at his facade of confidence. He fights back valiantly, but he's unsure about the answer to a few questions. You happen to know some of the answers but you also know the medical student code: never embarrass your classmates in front of an attending. All in all, he does pretty well, and your large medical team turns and walks down the hall, piling into the patient's room.

The fact that you are five people back from the patient's bed means that you can neither see nor hear what's going on. Since this isn't your patient, fighting the desire to zone out becomes difficult. Ultimately, you succumb to its power. After a few minutes and a quick attending exam, it's time to move on to the next patient. The attending scribbles a few notes and turns her attention to you. She doesn't say a word, but the message couldn't be clearer, so you reach into your white coat and grab your progress note. All attention is on you as you begin to talk about your patient, a three-year-old boy who presented with an acute asthma exacerbation. You begin to talk about how his older sister was sick last week, and then he got sick. You're going through the paces as no doubt you have seen many patients with this condition by now. You incidentally mention that the boy fell and hit his head as per his mother, but since this was after the asthma exacerbation started, you paid little attention to the fall. Unfortunately, the attending interrupts your next sentence before you can even finish it. "Did you ask if he had any loss of consciousness?" Your face begins to turn red since you know that she is not going to like your answer.

"No, I didn't."

"Well, did you ask about any vomiting or change in behavior?"

"No, I didn't really—"

She interrupts again. "What did the neuro exam show?"

You pause slightly: "I didn't really do a thorough exam."

Your attending shakes her head disappointedly as you fruitlessly try to put your derailed train of a presentation back on track. You follow her into the patient's room and watch as she asks the mother the questions you forgot to ask. You feel like a dog with its tail between its legs. Fortunately, all the answers to the questions the attending asks related to the fall are negative for any serious head trauma.

As she is leaving the room, the attending turns to you and says, "I agree with you that the child probably caught something from his sister and now has an asthma exacerbation." A wave of relief rushes over your body, but before you can relax, she asks, "So what classification of asthma does this patient fall into, and how would you treat it?" It takes ten seconds before the asthma treatment chart arises from your memory. For your attending, that is ten seconds too many. She proceeds to lecture "everyone" about the specifics of asthma treatment, without ever giving you a chance to show that you do know the answer, you just needed a moment. One of the residents is standing over the attending's shoulder, nodding at everything she says and staring at you with disappointment. Before finishing, your attending says, "I want you to prepare a five-minute presentation on this topic for tomorrow." *Great. Just what I wanted to do with all the free time I don't have,* you think. The nodding resident marks up your note, telling you to write this and not to write that. It seems you are falling out of grace with this medical team. *The next few weeks are gonna be rough,* you think. Taking a deep breath, you try to regain some confidence since you still must present two other patients. You can feel your anxiety rising, but you repeat the mantra "Just do the best you can; that is all you can do" and you begin to feel a little bit better.

The above vignette is a typical example of an awkward third-year medical student experience. At some point, despite your best efforts, you'll have an experience like the one described above. It's hard to be prepared for absolutely everything, and some situations are harder to read than are others. Even if you have a good feel for your patients, knowing the specific aspects of a patient's care that different attendings and residents will emphasize is hard. Many times you won't be quite up to snuff, but sometimes you'll go above and beyond your medical team's expectations. In other words, like any other activity, you'll have good days and bad days. Some days everything will fall into place, while other days everything will fall apart. The obvious goal is to minimize the "bad days" but know you'll never eliminate all of them. The sooner you accept the fact that perfection is impossible, the less bothered you'll be when things don't work out perfectly.

Tests and Grades

Achieving high marks during the third year is much less straightforward than it is during years one and two. During the first two years, if you did well on tests, you usually did well overall. In most medical schools, the third year calls for a lot more than good test grades.

Normally, a third-year clinical clerkship final grade is composed of assignments, an observed clinical exam, an end-of-the-rotation test, and the always-important subjective grade. It's hard to say which factors are most important because they have a tendency to differ between schools and clerkships. In one medical school, the test for surgery could be worth 50 percent of the final grade, while at another school it could be worth only 15 percent. Or at one medical school, the pediatric rotation could have the test count for 40 percent of the final grade, while the internal medicine rotation at the same school could say it's worth only 10 percent.

It's always a good idea to obtain the syllabus for a rotation before starting it. Glancing at the breakdown of grades only takes a minute and will provide guidance as to how to divide up your efforts. Of course, if you truly want a high grade, you'll need to do well in all aspects. But if time is limited, it makes more sense to focus on the factors that are worth a greater percentage of your grade. For example, if a rotation has assignments worth 40 percent of the grade and the test worth only 20 percent, it makes sense to spend your extra time making sure your write-ups are perfect rather than studying for the test.

You might also wish to seek out information on how the grades are reported on your transcript. Some schools give strictly pass or fail marks, while others use variants of the ABCDF system, with A equaling high honors, B equaling honors, C equaling pass, and so on. Some schools even report the exact percentage each student receives on a rotation. Some schools may report test grades, while others might not even mention them. Knowing this information will give you a better perspective as to how your efforts will be perceived by residency programs when they review your records.

Some rotations put much emphasis on assignments, while others don't even have them. The assignments you'll have for a given clerkship can range from patient write-ups to patient logs to research presentations and everything in between. But because assignments often make up a substantial portion of your grade, doing well on them is often paramount to your success, and the key to doing well on a third-year assignment is to figure out exactly what a professor wants. This can sometimes be a difficult task since assignment instructions are often nebulous. More times than not, the clerkship director will provide an outline of what is expected in an assignment, and while an outline is definitely useful, many details are often left out and figuring out exactly what to do to fulfill the assignment remains a challenge. The best solution to this problem is to find an example of an assignment that earned a perfect score. By studying this example, you'll be able to understand exactly what the professor is looking for. Some professors will provide examples of perfect scores, but if they don't, you can usually obtain one from the professor if you ask well in advance of the due date. If a professor can't provide an example, the next best option is to ask a friend who did well on the assignment.

Examining the grading rubric (if available) before you start the assignment is also useful as this will help you cover all the bases. For example, suppose a student was assigned to give a ten-minute presentation on appendicitis. Now imagine that in her presentation she covered appendicitis beautifully from its etiology to treatment. Unfortunately, she failed to include a research article because she wasn't aware that she had to. On the part of the grading rubric that covers research article presentation, she will get the lowest mark, but if she had examined the rubric in advance, she would have known she needed to include a research article in her presentation and her grade would have reflected this advance knowledge.

The clinical exam is another important component of your grade. Not every rotation has this component, and it is seldom worth a substantial portion of the grade. Nevertheless, for those rotations that do include a clinical exam, you'll want to do well. The observed clinical exam can run the gamut from picking a case at random to talk about to examining a real patient, and while this might sound more like a test than an assignment, it is usually graded more like an assignment than like a test.

Clinical exams that require students to examine a real patient can vary a great deal. You might end up getting a straightforward patient who is a good historian, but you might just as easily be assigned an impossibly complex patient who can't recall what he ate for breakfast. These exams call to mind Forrest Gump's well-known saying, "Life is like a box of chocolates. You never know what you're gonna get," and like life with all its complexities, such exams can be difficult to prepare for. Your interaction with the patient will depend upon your clinical knowledge, history-taking skills, physical exam skills, ability to integrate information, ability to generate a plan, and, of course, the patient.

Once again, the best way to prepare for this sort of exam is to get a copy of the grading rubric, which will allow you to study up on all the points you'll need to touch on. The grading rubric will almost always contain a section titled "Appropriate history and physical" or H&P. Every rotation has different nuances of the standard H&P, and every medical student should be aware of these. For instance, during a pediatric history for a young child, you should almost always ask about urinating, passing stool, feeding, and developmental behavior, but during a psychiatric history, this would usually be inappropriate. By the time you finish a rotation, the clinical experience you gain will help tremendously in your being familiar with the nuances of a rotation-specific H&P, but for testing purposes, it is never a bad idea to obtain a copy of a perfectly inclusive H&P checklist. Sometimes this checklist is the actual grading rubric.

The other types of observed clinical exams are usually more straightforward. Some will ask students to do a physical exam on a mannequin or a standardized patient. To study for this type of exam, you simply have to get a copy of the H&P checklist and make sure to hit every point on it. Instead of an observed physical exam, some rotations will ask a student to pick a case at random to talk about. The difficulty here is in the wide variety of cases you potentially might get stuck with. Luckily, usually the spectrum of possible cases is released before the exam, giving you the opportunity to study all of them in advance. These types of tests are impossible to study for without this advance opportunity, and if you find yourself in this situation, you have to just walk in and hope you're familiar with the cases you are assigned.

Most medical schools also require their students to keep a log of patients they have seen. Medical schools normally do this so they can collect data concerning all the differing diagnoses their students have experienced. Most of the time, patient logs are worth only a small percentage of your grade—if not 0 percent. The problem is that since they are required, if you fail to complete them, you'll generate a storm of e-mails and compliance meetings. The difficulty with logs is that many students allow too much time to elapse between seeing their patients and logging them in. If you wait too long, you may forget the details of your encounters with patients, or you might altogether forget to write up the log. This is especially true if you have a heavy patient load. Waiting a long time to write up the log will require you to spend more time trying to remember specifics, and your logs will likely be inaccurate. In the end, as irritating as logs can be, the easiest and most efficient way of doing a log is to complete it the same day you see the patient.

One aspect about the third year feels similar to your experience of the first two years of medical school, and that is the end-of-the-rotation test. Sometimes this test is a standardized test from the NBME (National Board of Medical Examiners), also known as a shelf exam, while some medical schools create their own tests. But before you begin to worry about an end-of-the-rotation test, find out if the rotation you're on even has one. Almost all third-year rotations will have some sort of test, but a few may not—in which case you can save yourself the anxiety of anticipating one. If a rotation does indeed have an exam, you'll want to figure out how the exam factors into your grade and how it is reported on your transcript. Some schools report their students' grades directly on the transcript—in particular shelf grades—while others won't even mention the grade. And as noted previously, some rotation exams will be worth a much greater percentage of your grade than will others.

If a rotation does have an NBME shelf exam, note that the grading is not linear. As with any standardized test, you'll never be able to find out how many questions you got right or wrong. The only information you'll be provided is how you match up with other medical students who took the same shelf at the exact same time. And like most standardized tests, the shelf is graded on a bell curve, with the mean scaled score of around 70 points and an average standard deviation of about 8 points. This means that if you took the test and got a scaled score of 70, you would be in the 50th percentile. If another student scored a 78 on the same test, or one standard deviation above the average, that student would be in the 86th percentile. A student who ended up scoring an 86, or two standard deviations above average, would be in the 98th percentile. (This assumes the mean is exactly 70 and the standard deviation is exactly 8.)

To complicate the situation, the means and the standard deviations of shelf exams vary by quarter and by rotation. The NBME understands that the farther along a medical student is in the third year, the more clinical knowledge that student will have. For instance, if you are taking your family medicine shelf but have already completed your pediatric, psychiatry, and ob/gyn rotations, you will have a huge advantage over a student who has not yet done those rotations. Grading both of you on the same bell curve would be unfair, so the means usually are progressively higher as the year goes on. For example, suppose the means for quarters one and two of the family medicine shelf are 70 and 74. And now suppose that one student took the test during the first quarter and got a score of 70, and a second student took the test during the second quarter and received a score of 70. The first student achieved the mean score and would be in the 50th percentile, while the second student would be in the 31st percentile because that score was half a standard deviation below the mean. Of course, the mean is seldom exactly 70, and the standard deviation is almost never exactly 8. Every quarter of every rotation will have different means and standard deviations, but the NBME publishes a chart every year based on past data that will equate your scaled score to a percentile, so all you must do is look at the NBME grading chart and see where you match up.

How the scores that you get are factored into your grade can vary. Some medical schools use a student's scaled score as a direct percentage, while others use the percentile as the grade. For example, suppose a student received a scaled score of 80 on a shelf, thereby putting her in the 90th percentile. One school might directly translate her scaled score into a grade, so for grading purposes, she would receive an 80 percent on the shelf. Other schools might give this same student a 90 percent on the shelf, equating to the percentile she is in.

So what does this shelf grading mumbo jumbo really mean? If your school bases its grading on the percentile score you achieve, the range of test grades is from 1 to 100, as with any other test. However, if your school bases grades directly on the scaled score, the range of possible grades will be smaller. The lowest possible grade you can get is around 55 because that is equivalent to the 1st percentile for most tests. And the highest grade you could achieve would be 99, which is approximately equivalent to the 99.99th percentile. This means that the diminishing returns are extreme (see chapter 3). For absolutely no effort you can earn a grade of 55 percent, while with all the effort in the world you could get a grade of 99 percent. The higher the scores, the more the returns diminish. The amount of work required to move from a scaled score of 90 (around the 99th percentile) to a scaled score of 99 (around the 99.99th percentile) is absurd. If you reflect on the fact that shelf exams may be only a small portion of your final grade, the idea is still more absurd. If a shelf is worth just 25 percent of your final grade, a scaled score of 90 would add 22.5 points onto your final grade, while a scaled score of 99 would add 25 points. The dizzying amount of extra studying required to go from a scaled score of 90 to 99 would thus add a mere 2.5 points to your final grade. Also, the shelf score must be considered in context of the entire grade, which normally has a large subjective component. The fact that the subjective grade is extremely variable means that it can easily offset all the work you do to obtain a higher shelf score. In other words, the subjective variability subsumes the shelf score variability and even further exacerbates the diminishing returns.

On a side note, every school has minimum passing requirements for its end-of-the-rotation tests. In the case of the shelf, you might technically have a passing grade in a rotation even if you score in the 5th percentile, but you could still fail the course because of poor performance. Grading aside, you will have to take the end-of-the-rotation test (unless there is none), and as for any other test, you'll want to do some studying. So how do you study for the shelf? Obviously, clinical experience will provide a fair amount of knowledge. However, the average end-of-the-rotation test or shelf exam will often include rare diseases not usually seen during a typical rotation. For example, during a typical pediatrics rotation you undoubtedly will see many cases of asthma and bronchiolitis but probably not a single case of congenital hypothyroidism or Edwards syndrome. So while you may be able to manage asthma and bronchiolitis perfectly, not having an expansive knowledge of rare diseases will hurt your grade on the final exam if it includes a case of Edwards syndrome. This means you'll have to study outside the hospital.

Studying

Although you'll have to study during the third year, a major advantage to this year is that you will be augmenting a knowledge base you've already built rather than creating one from scratch. Consider, for example, congestive heart failure. During your first two years in school you had to learn the anatomy of the heart, the physiology of the heart, the pathophysiology of congestive heart failure, and the drugs used to treat it. In your third year, with this base behind you, you need to learn only how to manage congestive heart failure. Even if you have forgotten some of what you learned previously, relearning something is easier than learning it for the first time. Of course, most medical school curricula focus heavily on internal medicine, and as a result, rotations such as ob/gyn and pediatrics aren't intensively covered during the first two years. This means that while doing those rotations, you'll need to do some extra studying, but the amount required pales in comparison to that required during your first two years.

Another sizeable difference between studying during the first two years and studying during the third year is the way in which information is presented. During the first two years, emphasis is placed on lecture slides, with every fact that appears on a lecture slide being fair game for tests. During the third year, however, you won't need to memorize any lecture slides. Although every rotation will have some mandatory lectures, and those lectures might include slides, the questions on the shelf exam will not be taken directly from those slides, so you won't need to memorize them. Also, third-year lectures normally are focused more on your personal gain than on items you must scrutinize in preparation for a test. Lecture information might well show up on a shelf exam, but that would be a coincidence.

If you became accustomed to using the lecture slides as your main source of studying during the first two years you will now have to find another source from which to study. Loved by some, hated by others, the main study materials for third-year medical students are books. Students who prefer to learn from books will, as a result, have an immediate advantage over those students who don't. Commonly, you'll hear first- or second-year students say, "I just can't sit down and read a book. I learn much better from lecture slides." These people will have a harder transition to third-year studying. If you're one of these types, know you'll have to adjust.

Books

Since you can choose from thousands of medical books, and some are much better than others, you'll want to learn how to find the right ones. Your first reflex may be to grab the biggest, most comprehensive reference book out there. The trouble is, books like this can be overwhelming and can lead to information overload. Reference books are good for looking up specific topics for a presentation, but they are far too all-encompassing to be useful for studying. Fortunately, books are made specifically for third-year clerkships, and these will tell you everything you need to know for a shelf exam, with little extraneous information. You can use these books as reference material as well, but it is not uncommon for a student to read them all the way through. Still, among the third-year clerkship books you'll find a large variety from which to choose, and finding the right ones may be a challenge. The best method for selecting the books that will be right for you is to ask those students who came before you and did well on the shelf exam which books they used. You'll usually find a consensus as to which books are best.

Practice Questions

Apart from books, the other major study resource is practice questions. Vital for any standardized test, practice questions provide the best way to test your knowledge while you become familiar with the format of the test. You can find these in books or access them online. Of course, not all practice questions are created equal. Again, the easiest way to find the best source of practice questions is to ask students who did well on the shelf exam which practice questions they used.

Most practice questions provide an explanation, sometimes lengthy, about why the right answer is right and why the wrong answers are wrong. Some students make the mistake of not reading the explanation of answers they get right, believing that they already know what the explanation will be. Always read the explanations. Oftentimes you'll find bits of information in the explanation you didn't know, despite your correct answer. Another mistake students make is not reading the books they select in their entirety; too often students rely entirely on practice questions. Despite their usefulness, practice questions often do not cover all the necessary details of a topic and are designed simply to test the base of knowledge you will gain from books and clinical experience. Using only practice questions will create a spotty knowledge base—you'll be strong in some areas and lacking entirely in others. It's much like trying to paint a room by dipping a paintbrush in a can of paint and then flinging the paint against the wall. The room won't be evenly painted, and you'll find missed spots everywhere. Reading a book is the equivalent of painting a solid, even base coat.

Although the methods of studying during the third year are somewhat different from the methods used during the first two years, the principles of effective studying are the same:

- Learning the concepts and pathophysiology is paramount.

- You must try to avoid cramming as it is inefficient and usually leads to poor long-term retention.

- The principle of diminishing returns still holds.

- You can help yourself avoid procrastination and anxiety by creating a reasonable study schedule.

Utilizing the above principles to study will result in your learning the relevant knowledge in the least amount of time, with the greatest long-term retention, and with the smallest amount of anxiety. In other words, you'll attain maximum efficiency.

Effective Studying in the Third Year

Two minor differences between effective studying in the third year and in the first and second years are worth mentioning. Through clinical experience, every day as a third-year medical student you will come across topics with which you are unfamiliar. These can range from not understanding why a certain test is used to not knowing the proper management of a disease to knowing nothing altogether about a specific disease. You will want to make sure that once these gaps in knowledge are exposed, they're filled as soon as possible. If, for example, it turns out that a patient's pregnancy is complicated by placenta accreta, and you have no idea what in the world that is, you should immediately study that topic. Not knowing a critical piece of knowledge is frustrating to the average medical student, and this frustration can be a great motivation to study.

The real advantage to studying an unknown topic as it becomes exposed is that you'll quickly connect your book knowledge to a real-life clinical experience. This provides great long-term retention. For example, suppose a mother gave birth to a baby who had gastroschisis (an abdominal wall defect in which the contents of the abdomen protrude freely outside the body). Now imagine a third-year medical student who didn't know a thing about gastroschisis watching the birth of a baby with the intestines hanging outside the abdomen. No doubt this experience would leave an indelible image in that student's mind. Now suppose this student decided to go home that day and read all about gastroschisis. Every single detail about gastroschisis he reads will be intimately connected to his physical experience of the disease. And since the physical experience was so memorable, all the details he learns as he reads will be too. Reading about a topic soon after you have a clinical experience with it is a highly efficient way to achieve long-term retention of knowledge. Take advantage of this whenever possible.

During the first two years of medical school, students' knowledge is assessed only on specific days—test days. This means that for weeks leading up to an exam, first- or second-year medical students can be clueless about topics they are supposed to know, but this is perfectly acceptable as long as when the day of the test arrives, they know everything. In many cases, this is exactly what happens since, as discussed, many medical students are crammers. Despite the inefficiency of cramming, many students continue to study this way out of habit, and the fact that their test scores can be just as good as those of students who don't cram only serves to inspire the habit. Unfortunately for crammers, the situation during the third year is decidedly different.

During the third year, your knowledge will be assessed continuously in multifarious clinical situations. Every single day, attendings and residents will ask their medical students clinical questions to assess their clinical knowledge and to provide teaching points. If a student decides to start studying only a few days before the shelf exam, that student will seem lacking in knowledge to the medical team in the previous weeks—yet another reason to avoid cramming.

The Subjective Component

Moving past assignments and tests, we come to the element of third-year grading that makes it unique: the subjective component. The subjective component can comprise up to 50 percent of your clerkship grade, which means you can do well on your rotation assignments and the shelf exam but receive a poor grade because of the subjective element. The average incoming third-year medical student has seldom encountered a grading scheme quite like this since the whole concept of grading a group of people in the first two years of medical school lies in standardization and objectivity. Measuring one person's intellectual progress against another's would be next to impossible unless everyone was taking the same tests and completing the same assignments. It is impossible to know how much students know and how much they don't unless they are asked—hence the tests and assignments.

But during the third year, you won't be just sitting in class listening to lectures. You will be part of a medical team and your behavior will be observed and judged by everyone around you. In some clinical situations, your team might perceive you as doing well, while in others, you might be seen as doing less well. To capture a picture of a third-year medical student's clinical acumen, medical schools introduce a subjective component to the grading scheme in which the medical team that has observed you will be asked how "good" you are.

To introduce some level of standardization to a subjective process, most medical schools have a grading rubric that an attending or resident must fill out about the student being observed. In an ideal world, an attending or resident would observe the way in which the student handles herself clinically and would accurately assess her medical skills and knowledge according to the rubric. To best prepare for this aspect of grading, the first step is to get a copy of the school's grading rubric for a specific rotation—something that is normally readily available. Grading rubrics usually consist of a series of categories such as history taking skills, physical examination skills, and case presentation skills but can also include more nebulous categories such as patient advocacy or communications and relationships. Each category contains a range of grades you might receive, usually on a scale from 1 to 5. For instance, the description above the grade of 1 for a category might read, "Unacceptable. This student in no way meets any of the criteria for a third-year medical student." The description above the grade of 3 could read something like, "Student meets appropriate standards for a third-year medical student," and the description above the grade of 5 might read, "The abilities this student possesses are truly rare and are easily among the top in the class." The grades of 2 and 4 of course would fall somewhere in between the other grades. Having a copy of the grading rubric will provide you with a good idea of the expectations you'll need to meet to achieve high marks. Usually a rubric also includes a space at the bottom where an attending or resident can write an opinion of a student.

Since the subjective component is worth a substantial portion of the final grade, you will want to know how the evaluations you receive are numerically computed. This computation can in fact be complicated. Most rotations have more than one attending or resident filling out evaluations, so questions arise:

- Does the school weigh every evaluation equally, or are some more important than others?

- If a student spent more time with one attending than another, would each evaluation hold the same weight?

- If a student receives one very bad evaluation among a multitude of good ones, will the school consider the bad one an outlier and discard it?

- How do the grades of 1 through 5 translate into the final subjective grade? For example, some schools will view an evaluation composed of all 3s as worth 80 percent, while others will view it as worth 60 percent.

In other words, the situation is not straightforward, and the formula to determine subjective grades can differ even between rotations. You probably won't be able to get the answers to these questions from your attendings or residents. They simply fill out the forms and give them to the course coordinator. The person who will know the answers is the course coordinator—who actually takes the evaluations and enters the grades into the computer system—so direct your questions to this individual. Also ask the course coordinator which attendings or residents actually fill out the evaluations. If you are working with a single attending or resident, this answer will be obvious, but more commonly students will work with multiple attendings and residents over the course of a rotation, and it's difficult to know who will fill out their evaluations. Individual students know with whom they have spent the majority of their time, but the school might not know this, so to avoid surprises, find out early on who fills out the evaluations.

Once you are familiar with the grading scheme, you'll want to know how you can do well in the clinical setting. Many incoming third-year students think if they are knowledgeable, have a good bedside manner, take good H&Ps, write good notes, and work extra hours, they will earn a great subjective grade. As in previous years, most believe that the best will rise to the top. In fact, a common secret belief of many incoming third-year students is that those who are primarily "book smart" and not particularly socially adept will do less well. Ideally, students would be judged purely on their clinical skills and knowledge. That would be fair.

But the very nature of subjective grading means that it is inherently unfair. However, you can use several tactics to help you do well in your clinical rotations. In short, you'll want to be professional. This means showing up on time, dressing appropriately, and making a good first impression—these skills are as important in the clinical setting as they are in any other sort of interaction. Every person on the medical team will expect professional behavior from all others from the time they show up until the time they leave. And of course you have just one chance to make a first impression. This may require you to get up a little earlier on your first day to make sure you have time to groom yourself well and to arrive on time. Giving up a few minutes of sleep is well worth avoiding a bad first impression.

Simply put, students who do well clinically go above the expectations of their medical team. General expectations naturally vary from one medical team to the next, and doctors from different specialties emphasize different aspects of the history, the physical exam, and patient care. For example, a general surgeon might not care much about the cardiovascular aspect of the physical exam, while a cardiologist might care only about the cardiovascular exam. Therefore, a cursory cardiovascular exam may be more than sufficient during your surgical rotation and highly inappropriate during your cardiology rotation. It doesn't take much effort to figure out that if you are working with a cardiologist, taking a full cardiac history and physical will benefit you. You would be mistaken to get into the habit of doing a cursory cardiovascular exam and not altering that practice when the time calls for a better one. Still, even among specialties, expectations can vary greatly. One medical team may prefer that you take full histories every time, while another team may want only focused histories. One attending or resident may desire you to write a note in a specific way, which another attending abhors.

The point is that expectations vary among attendings and residents and it is impossible to know them a priori. Many students make the mistake of guessing what their medical team wants, but guessing wrong can result in your not meeting the team's expectations. The best way to avoid this calamity is to ask your attendings and residents what their expectations are—even before you lay eyes on your first patient. This will give you an idea of which parts of the clinical exam you should emphasize, how to present your patient, and what to include in your note. Asking your attendings or residents for a copy of one of their notes is never a bad idea as it may provide you a stellar template. Usually, if it's good enough for them, it's good enough.

If you are unable to discuss the expectations before doing your first clinical exam, you'll be forced to guess. If faced with this situation, you should err on the side of caution by doing a thorough H&P and writing a thorough note. This will lower the probability of your not asking the patient the right questions or missing something on the physical exam.

In such instances, the worst thing the team will say about you is that you need not be so thorough. It's easier for an attending or resident to fault a student for not being thorough enough.

Another common mistake medical students often make is not asking their attendings or residents for feedback concerning their clinical performance. Normally, when things seem to be going well, they usually are, but there is always a chance you're doing a subpar job without even knowing you are. An attending may not be impressed with your clinical skills and knowledge but not think or care enough to tell you this. One of the last things that any third-year medical student wants to see is an evaluation that says, "By the way, you did a crappy job. I just wanted to tell you this at the last possible moment so that you have no time to make improvements during this rotation." Unfortunately, you'll normally receive a written evaluation about your performance only at the end of the rotation. To avoid a surprise, regularly ask your team for feedback. It is never a bad idea to ask your attendings or residents if your histories, physicals, notes, and presentations are good and what you might do to improve them or if you can make any improvements in general. Tell your attending that you want to get the highest marks you can and ask what is necessary to achieve this. Some attendings and residents have a nebulous idea of what behavior constitutes a top mark, and satisfying ill-defined expectations is impossible. But asking the medical team what you need to do to obtain a high grade will force them to consider what behavior constitutes a top mark and will help define concrete goals you can work to achieve. Don't rely on hearsay by asking a peer who has completed the rotation already; ask your team directly.

Unfortunately, even those who follow the above guidelines might not earn a great subjective grade. It is naive to assume that your attendings or residents are grading you based only on clinical skills. Often, two students with equivalent clinical skills and knowledge can end up with entirely different subjective grades because while your attendings and residents are supposed to observe your clinical performance and compare this to the performance of other students with whom they have worked and then grade accordingly, what actually happens can be entirely different. In the end, such grading is subjective, or as Merriam-Webster describes it, "based on feelings or opinions rather than facts." This means that attendings and residents will grade you based on their personal feelings and opinions about you, and these opinions aren't always based on your clinical performance. An attending might like one of your peers because they both attend the same church or because they're both basketball players, or he might dislike that same person for no good reason.

The nature of the subjective component necessarily introduces a high level of variability into the third-year grading scheme. This variability automatically includes a level of unfairness. This subjective unfairness can take place even before you meet your attending for the first time! For example, one attending might think that an average third-year medical student performance deserves a grade of 3/5, while another might think that the same performance deserves a 5/5. This means that from the outset, the second attending is more inclined to give better grades than the first. Now suppose you're lucky enough to work with the attending who gives high marks, but your good friend has the unfortunate luck of working with the attending with the tendency to give lower grades. Probability says you will get a much better subjective grade than your friend. He might have to win the Nobel Prize to receive the same grade you received by simply doing an average job.

What's almost worse is that some attendings and residents view the grading rubric as just another piece of pesky paperwork, and they may fill it out as fast as they can without caring—this usually results in a completely average evaluation. Attendings with this practice are known for giving everyone the same grade and writing very little in the comment section. You might indeed make a landmark medical discovery but still end up with the same grade as everyone else if this attending is marking you. In short, in some situations the cards have already been dealt, and no matter what you do or don't do, the results will be the same.

As discussed above, the root of unfairness in subjective grading lies in an attending's or resident's personal feelings about a student, and so, despite the clinical acumen you may possess, many evaluations will be based on how much an attending or resident likes you. Imagine this scenario: The lease on your apartment is about to run out, and your girlfriend has just moved in to live with you. As she unpacks suitcase after suitcase, your spacious one-bedroom apartment feels more and more cramped. Every bone in your body is saying that you need to move into a bigger place. You haven't lived in the area long, and you need help finding a new apartment. One of your friends suggests moving into her apartment complex, which seems like a good idea until you remember that your friend is wealthy and there is no way you can afford the kind of rent she can. Fortunately, two different real estate agents work in the area, and since you don't know which is better, you decide to give both a try.

While the first real estate agent is showing off apartments, the conversation turns to the fact that you both climbed Mount Kilimanjaro in the spring of 2008. From that moment on, this real estate agent feels like a long-lost buddy. You discover you like the same sports teams and the same restaurants, and you share many similar philosophies of life. Before parting, he asks you out to dinner as a gesture of friendship. You've found not just a new apartment but a new best friend!

Even though your search for an apartment seems to you to have come to an end, your girlfriend disagrees. On to real estate agent number two. This real estate agent is professional and shows you three nice apartments—apartments just as nice as those your new best friend showed you. The only difference is that real estate agent number two never climbed Mount Kilimanjaro and doesn't like the same sports teams you like. In fact, you don't even know what sports teams this real estate agent likes because your conversation never veered from apartment talk.

In the end, you don't change apartment complexes because when your landlord learns you planned to move, he offers you a huge incentive to move into a bigger apartment in the same complex. The offer is too good to turn down. The very next week one of your medical school friends begins looking to move and has time to see only one real estate agent. Which one are you going to recommend? Obviously, though the agents are equally competent, you are going to recommend your new best friend. If you were asked to evaluate the two, your new best buddy agent would almost certainly achieve higher marks. You would score your new best friend higher, even though as far as ability and professionalism go, the two are equal, and your score would be unfair to agent number two.

Now picture an attending or resident who is writing up evaluations on two clinically equivalent medical students—one is a new best buddy, the other simply an acquaintance. Certainly in the same way you gave higher marks to your best buddy real estate agent, the best friend medical student will receive higher marks. Helping someone you like rather than someone you don't know well is only human nature, and since third-year grading is subjective, an attending or resident likely won't be able to separate out personal feelings about a student when writing up an evaluation. This doesn't mean you won't receive good evaluations if you're not best of friends with your attendings. Rather, it means that if all other factors are equal, you will receive a better evaluation if you make friendly connections with those who are grading you. Some attendings and residents will be better than others at separating out their personal feelings while evaluating students, but even the most professional will not be immune from the influences of personal feelings.

So the question becomes, How can I get my attending or resident to like me? The answer is complicated indeed because it lies in human nature and is related to context. Surely you have, throughout your life, met people with whom you became friends and others with whom you did not. Why do you become friends with one person but not another? Simply stated, you choose the people you like to be your friends, and the people you like are generally those who give you positive feelings when you're around them. Usually this is because you can relate to each other in many spheres—that is, you share feelings and ideals. What does this have to do with medical school? Along the way, you are bound to meet people with whom you get along and people with whom you don't.

Although many aspects of your personal relationship with your attending or resident are out of your control, you can make an effort to create positive feelings. Some students will suck up—that is, they'll align all their interests with their perception of their superior's interests and will make every effort to spin their comments to please the superior. They do this in the hope that it will make their superior like them. This method can have mixed results, depending on how obvious the suck-up is and how much the attending or resident enjoys flattery. Theoretically, if a student is sly and an attending or resident is pompous, this method will work. But sucking up can negatively affect a student if the attending views the suck-up's comments and actions as insincere. Sucking up might help you obtain a better grade, but your peers will hold you in contempt. Besides, who wants to be known as a brown-noser?

You can inspire an attending or resident to like you in far more sincere ways. One easy way is to make your team's life easier. We naturally look favorably on those who make our lives easier and more manageable. Sometimes a medical student can feel like the proverbial anchor the medical team has to drag throughout the day, while other times the student will be assigned tasks that, if completed, will save the team time. If you conduct a great history and physical on rounds and write a phenomenal note, the attending or resident will certainly be able to see the patient faster. And helpfulness does not necessarily have to be relegated to the medical sphere. For example, fixing an attending's computer is a great way to earn brownie points, particularly for those older attendings who aren't computer savvy. This isn't to suggest that you ought to ask every attending if she is having computer trouble or every resident if he needs his laundry done. However, if the situation arises when you might be of use to your attending or resident, offer help and you'll cast yourself in a positive light.

Of course, your attending's computer may be in perfect working order and your resident's laundry may be done. Your medical team might not want you to write notes, or they might repeat the entire history and physical despite the fact that you've already done them. Your duties may be relegated to simply shadowing, and in such cases you'll have little opportunity to offer help. Still, recognizing that a student with more responsibilities will have a greater chance to help the team than will one with fewer responsibilities will enable you to assess the situation clearly. The number of responsibilities your team gives you often depends in large measure on the trust an attending or resident has in you, but if your attending or resident is neurotic, he might be distrustful and give you few responsibilities. Remember, though, this isn't a static situation. If you do an exemplary job with whatever duties you have, your team's trust in you will rise, which may generate more responsibility for you and a greater potential to help the team. Showing a resident or attending that you have studied, that you are interested in your patients, and that you are willing to take initiative by anticipating the next step in a patient's care will no doubt make the team feel more comfortable about giving you more patient responsibilities. Acting aloof, uninterested, and unmotivated will only prove to do the opposite.

One quick aside: Never lie about what you did or didn't do during a clinical exam. Sometimes you might forget to check a lab value or clinical exam result, and instead of telling your attending or resident you didn't check, you'll be tempted to say it was normal or to just make up something to avoid casting yourself in a negative light. Remember, most reports are easy to check, and if an attending or resident finds out you've lied even once, you will be considered forever unreliable and untrustworthy. This healthy distrust will be fueled by the fact that a patient's health is at stake and the attending is ultimately the responsible party. If on a clinical exam you forget to ask a question or check a quantity and your attending or resident asks you about it, the best response is, "I don't know. I forgot to check it. I'll look it up right now." This happens to every medical student at least once, and although you might fear that such an error makes you appear incompetent, telling the truth is always the best path to take.

Appearing to be enthusiastic about whatever rotation you happen to be on will also help your attending or resident to look favorably upon you. At one point in time, the attendings and residents on a specific medical service decided that out of all the specialties, this was the one for them. Of course, some choose a specialty specifically for the money they can earn, but most choose a specialty because they feel passionate about it. Those who teach are usually the most passionate, so showing enthusiasm for a certain specialty and sharing in the attendings' and residents' passion will help you to establish a better connection. Say, for example, that you are a general surgery attending, and a patient with a textbook presentation of appendicitis has just arrived under your care. Now imagine that you coincidentally gave a lecture on appendicitis to two medical students earlier that day. The first medical student's eyes widen in shock, and she immediately rushes excitedly over to the patient to see the physical example of appendicitis. In contrast, the second medical student expresses no excitement and lazily makes his way to the patient's bed. Which student would you look upon more favorably? Obviously, the student who shares your passion would win your appreciation.

Maintaining Enthusiasm

A third-year medical student may have difficulty maintaining enthusiasm throughout the year. Almost all students begin brimming with enthusiasm at finally being in the hospital and no longer studying for Step 1. But as the year progresses, the many consecutive 5:00 a.m. wake-ups and late nights can dull that enthusiasm. As time passes, students become more tired and less excited and surely will find some rotations simply not interesting, though these will vary from student to student. One medical student might find nothing more boring than having to say, over and over, "Your child has a sinus infection—it's probably viral," while another might detest standing for hours on end holding retractors during a long surgical case.

Despite the difficulties, you must make the effort to maintain your enthusiasm. Nothing is more detrimental to this mind-set than saying, "I hate this rotation and can't wait until it ends." Even entertaining such thoughts will quell your enthusiasm. The best step to take is to replace such negative thoughts with positive ones. You'll have an opportunity to learn in every rotation, to grow as a physician and a person. A student who dislikes ob/gyn, for instance, might still experience great joy in delivering a baby, while a student who isn't so keen on surgery might still get a thrill out of being a part of a life-saving operation.

Throughout the third year, every medical student will have to answer the following question ad nauseam: "So what specialty do you want to go into?" During the early months of the third year, most medical students have only a foggy idea of the answer to this question, though some know with 100 percent certainty. The supercompetitive specialties attract those who are more certain—for instance, it's tough to decide at the end of the third year that you want to go into dermatology unless you have a stunning résumé or are willing to take a year off after your third year to do research. Of course, some students knew their specialty of interest even before starting school—for example, a few have wanted to be pediatricians since they were ten years old and ever since have been in hot pursuit of this goal. Whatever your situation at the start of the third year, know that a perfectly acceptable response to the question about your specialty interest is "I'm not sure yet."

If you happen to know which specialty you desire, should you let your medical team know if you are doing a rotation that is not of interest to you? For instance, if you know you wish to go into orthopedics and you're working with an outpatient pediatrician, should you tell him about your desire? This is a tightrope walk. It's never a good idea to lie, but some attendings and residents will judge you harshly for picking certain specialties. If you are open about your preference, you risk revealing your lack of enthusiasm, and this may be reflected in your evaluation. If, say, your attending is a pediatrician who disdains surgeons and you mention you want to specialize in surgery, she may think you don't give a damn about pediatrics, and you risk her wondering why she ought to give you a good evaluation. Some students might go so far as to tell the pediatrician they want to go into pediatrics, while telling the cardiologist that they want to go into cardiology. This is a morally questionable practice, and of course every attending and resident is different, but I believe the best course of action lies somewhere between telling outright lies and guarding the truth. Even those who are 100 percent certain of their desired specialty might possibly change their mind in a future rotation. They might conceivably wind up hating the rotation of the specialty they initially wanted. Do not discount the influences of future experiences. I believe the best approach is to tell the attending or resident who asks what specialty you are interested in that you're not yet sure. If the follow-up question comes—"Well, do you have any inkling of what you want to do?"—talk about what you liked and disliked about your previous rotations and let the person know you're still trying to keep an open mind.

Remember, you are at the mercy of the subjective grade, and it's next to impossible to make up for a lousy subjective evaluation. Following the above guidelines will certainly help you do the best you can, but still, sometimes situations are out of your control. Sometimes, you'll find no way to overcome the subjective unfairness of the third-year grading system. Many medical students enter the third year with the misconception that working extra hours will earn them a better grade. Unfortunately, this isn't always the case. The relationship between a student and an attending or resident is complex, and the final subjective grade might not always correlate with the work you do.

Summary

Love it or hate it, a substantial portion of your third-year grades will have more to do with whether or not your medical team likes you than with your clinical knowledge and skills. Most medical students who receive the short end of the stick as far as subjective evaluations go become understandably frustrated, which is compounded by the fact that these students often have been at the top of the academic heap throughout their entire lives. They may be unaccustomed to receiving average marks, and burnout, loss of enthusiasm, and even depression might result. You definitely do not want to suffer burnout or depression, but bear in mind that the subjective system of third-year grading creates a real possibility that this can happen.

To avoid this trap, be aware that grades are not the most important attainment from a medical school rotation. The whole point of a clinical rotation is for you to augment your clinical knowledge and skills while learning to be a doctor. Your focus should be not on grades but on the knowledge and experience you are gaining. Most of the rotations you'll do in the third year will be your last chance to learn in this supportive type of environment. For example, unless you're going into psychiatry, your psychiatry rotation will probably be the last time that you ever see patients in this context. Try to reap the most from the rotation during the limited time you're in it. In the years to come, you're not likely to remember your final grade in your psychiatry rotation, but chances are that you'll remember the unique experiences you had and some of the knowledge you obtained. If you are having difficulty resisting the lure of focusing on grades, you might try the following mental exercise.

Think back to a bad grade you got in high school or college, and recall how disappointed you were at the time. Now think about how much you care about that grade today. You'll surely discover you probably don't care at all. Now imagine how you will feel about your third-year grades once you are well into your residency. Chances are that you'll barely think about them. So why get worked up about them now? If at the end of the day you know you have put forth your best effort and that you've done all that you could have done, there's no point in worrying. Worrying will only cause unneeded anxiety.

And so, as you begin your third year, remember that this year is designed for you to gain knowledge and develop your clinical skills. Trying to earn points that are often impossible to earn is a no-win game and will create anxiety and worry you needn't experience. The third year is a unique learning experience, and if you keep your focus on that learning, you'll experience nothing but success!

8 | Studying for the USMLE Step 2 CK

I can't believe I slept through the whole night, you think to yourself. Strangely, the wretched beep of your alarm clock causes a sigh of relief. Slowly you sit up on the side of your bed and let your feet feel the ground for the first time today. Next time I lie down in this bed, this test will be behind me. The thought is comforting. The fact that you slept uneventfully through the night is a huge success. You can remember how much anxiety you had the night before the Step 1 and how that anxiety didn't let you sleep. To make the situation worse, not being able to fall asleep only created more anxiety, which made sleeping almost impossible.

While it's true you didn't study nearly as much for this test as for the Step 1, you still managed to get through a lot of material over the past three weeks. Thankfully the Step 2 CK has far less minutiae compared to its predecessor, which made studying for it a whole lot less psychosis inducing. You find it hard to not compare this day with the day you took the Step 1. As you steadily make your way through your morning routine, you notice that something feels different. You feel relaxed. The Step 1 is like the SAT of medical school, while the importance of the Step 2 CK is still somewhat questionable. In fact, some residency programs don't even need to see a Step 2 CK score before they send out interviews! The thought is relaxing. That doesn't mean you want to do poorly—just that the pressure is off.

A deep sigh leaves your lips as you take one last look at your backpack, making sure that everything you need for the day is there: ID, second ID (just in case), granola bars, water bottles, scheduling permit, and an extra pair of underwear. You don't really know why you always bring an extra pair of underwear, but the fact that you do provides a strange feeling of comfort.

Turning your key in the ignition causes the digital glow of your car's clock to light up as the engine rumbles to life. A quick calculation reveals that you have exactly one hour to make a twenty-minute trip. You have never been late for a standardized test and you don't want to start with this one. Eighteen minutes later you find yourself safely nestled into a rather good parking spot in front of the testing center.

As you briskly make your way into the testing center, you notice (as is always the case in medical school) that you are not the first one to arrive. Fortunately you also notice a couple of your good medical school friends sitting in the testing lobby, with notes splayed all over their laps. For the moment you avoid saying hi because you just want to get checked in and claim a locker for the day. After a quick five minutes of ID showing and fingerprinting, you make your way toward your friends. Even though you see study material everywhere, no studying is taking place. Rather than talking about the test, all the students seem to be expressing their excitation and fears of their upcoming specialty-specific fourth-year rotations. You can remember this same moment before the Step 1, when the tension was almost palpable. This is much different.

After you spend a few minutes in friendly conversation, one of the proctors makes the announcement for everyone to line up and enter the testing center. The conversation dies almost immediately as you all obediently form a line. You feel the anxiety in your gut, and you roll your head sideways to crack your neck. The time has come to take this test. As you are about to enter the glass aquarium full of test takers, one thought seems to reverberate in your mind: *Let's get this over with.*

An adage in medical school sums up the studying needed for Steps 1, 2, and 3: "Two months, two weeks, and two number two pencils." Despite the fact that tests these days are computer based, this adage holds (mostly) true. Step 3 is a test normally taken during one's first year of residency and is beyond the scope of this book. The main concern in this chapter is the USMLE Step 2 Clinical Knowledge (Step 2 CK).

The Step 2 CK exam has the same format as the Step 1 exam except it has eight question sections instead of seven. As is clear from its name, the USMLE Step 2 CK tests the knowledge you have gained primarily during the third year. Many questions on topics related to internal medicine, as well as to pediatrics, surgery, ob/gyn, psychiatry, family medicine, and neurology will appear. You may have some questions about subject matter not normally covered in a third-year rotation—orthopedics and dermatology, for example—but those questions are few in number compared to those related to topics of the major third-year rotations.

The biggest question about this test is when to take it. Every medical student has to take and pass the Step 1 before starting the third year, but the Step 2 CK has no similar restrictions. In fact, most medical schools simply require students to take this test before graduation. This means that if you decide to take it close to the end of your fourth year, residency programs won't even see the score until you've already been matched to a program. Superficially speaking, taking it late in the year makes sense since it creates a no-pressure situation. Who wants to torture themselves with step studying again?

Unfortunately, a few issues arise when you decide to take the Step 2 CK late in the fourth year. The first is that residency programs are starting to place more emphasis on the Step 2 CK. Granted at present, less emphasis is placed on the Step 2 CK than on the Step 1, but that practice is changing. More competitive specialties and residency programs seem to be at the forefront of this movement as they begin to look for other ways of differentiating candidates who appear to be otherwise equal. A few programs even require that the Step 2 CK be taken before you make an application, so taking it late will automatically exclude you from applying to certain residency programs. If you take the Step 2 CK toward the end of the fourth year, you might also be suffering from senioritis. The second half of the fourth year is considered to be the easiest time in medical school—few (if any) assignments or tests and thus little studying. Combining this with the fact that a typical fourth-year student has already applied and interviewed for residency can create the perfect storm of apathy. After three and a half years of striving to do well, the average fourth-year medical student now desires only to pass. Drumming up the motivation to study for and take a colossal standardized test can be difficult when you've already lost the motivation to do almost anything else.

Taking the test later in the year also means the test will be more challenging since you'll have forgotten some of the material from rotations you completed over a year earlier. Since the fourth year normally gives a fair amount of elective time, many fourth-year medical students will start to "specialize," meaning they are likely to take electives in their chosen field. While you may thus be particularly knowledgeable in a specific area, you'll likely begin to forget the knowledge from other areas. And if you haven't done a recent rotation in ob/gyn or pediatrics, the specifics will be hard to remember. This means that as the year advances, studying for the Step 2 CK takes more effort.

On the other side of the coin, taking the Step 2 CK test is easier at the beginning of fourth year because the knowledge you gained in third-year rotations will still be fresh in your mind and you'll likely be more motivated. One of the greatest benefits of taking the test earlier in the year is that you can take it and forget it. The application process can make the fourth year a stressful time with the ERAS (Electronic Residency Application Service), away rotations in foreign environments, interviews, and travel arrangements, and worrying about another huge standardized test hanging over your head is the last thing you need.

Most medical students who take the Step 2 CK on the earlier side are glad they did.

Of course, taking the test early will add the stress created from your desire to do well. Knowing that residency programs will see your scores will put a little extra fuel on the fire. To solve this problem, many students choose to take the Step 2 CK after the automatic release of test scores. Currently, the scores of anyone who takes the Step 2 CK before a certain date (usually toward the beginning of the academic year) will automatically be released to residency programs. After said date, you can choose whether or not you wish to release your scores to residency programs. This enables you to see your score before you decide if you want it released, and for those who don't want to risk a poor score adversely affecting their applications, this choice relieves much stress. Again, some residency programs may require a Step 2 CK score before considering an application complete, and there is some uncertainty about how the Step 2 CK results will affect your application. Can you make up for a poor Step 1 performance with a good Step 2 performance? It's hard to say for sure, and I'm willing to bet every residency program views the Step 2 CK slightly differently. The fact is, there's no single perfect time to take the Step 2 CK. See how your fourth-year schedule ends up and determine when you'll have a reasonable amount of free time to study for the exam.

Mention Step 1 to any doctor or medical student and he'll probably close his eyes and groan as if experiencing acute stomach pain. Mention the Step 2 CK to any doctor or medical student and you'll likely hear, "Oh yeah, Step 2. It wasn't so bad. Not nearly as bad as Step 1." Most things—well, almost anything—looks good compared to Step 1, and that includes the Step 2 CK. The main difference is that the Step 2 CK requires you to recall clinical knowledge rather than absurd numbers of details. Remembering details based on clinical experience is far easier than remembering them from studying an overly detailed chart that seems to have no pattern. A perfect example of the kind of detailed knowledge required in a Step 1 question follows:

> A four-year-old girl was out camping with her family and was bitten by a bat.
>
> What is the genetic makeup of the virus she would most likely be infected with?
> A. Single-stranded DNA
> B. Double-stranded DNA
> C. Single-stranded RNA
> D. Double-stranded RNA

The average medical student likely knows that bats are a source of rabies, so you can deduce that the virus in question is most likely the rabies virus. What the average medical student wouldn't know (unless she were in the midst of Step 1 studying or just learned about it in a lecture) is the genetic makeup of the rabies virus. This detail has no consequence on any decision a doctor might have to make in the foreseeable future, yet this is the kind of detail that makes studying for Step 1 a challenge. Figuring out the genetic makeup of the rabies virus cannot be done using logic. The only way to confidently answer this question is if you have memorized a chart of viruses and their genetic makeups. If this were a Step 2 CK question, it might read as follows:

> A four-year-old girl was out camping with her family and was bitten by a bat. She is up to date on the standard childhood vaccinations.
>
> What is the appropriate course of action?
> A. No treatment necessary
> B. Rabies vaccine administration
> C. Rabies immune globulin administration
> D. Administration of rabies vaccine and immune globulin

Knowing how to treat a rabies bite is important because the right action could potentially save the patient's life. Remembering this detail would be especially easy if you had encountered a case of rabies in the clinical setting and could tie the question to an actual experience. Because these questions are clinically based, for most students the Step 2 CK facts take far less effort to retain than do Step 1 facts.

Most students tend to do better on the Step 2 CK than they did on Step 1. Step 1 encompasses everything you've learned during your first two years, while the Step 2 CK focuses primarily on the knowledge gained during the third year. This means that overall you're covering less material, and since clinical knowledge is easier to retain, you won't need to study as hard for the Step 2 CK as you did for Step 1. On average, students study for two to three weeks for the Step 2 CK as compared to one to two months for Step 1. In addition, since the tests are identically formatted, you're one test experience ahead of the game when you sit down to take the Step 2 CK.

How do you study for the Step 2 CK? The strategy is similar to studying for Step 1. First, learn the material during your clinical rotations. Of course, seeing everything related to a subject in the span of the average rotation—four to six weeks—is almost impossible. And since most rotations have an end-of-the-rotation test that covers a large body of information, if you wish to do well on the tests and therefore your rotations (see chapter 7, "Clerkships"), you'll want to study outside of class. Second, find someone who did well on the Step 2 CK and ask how that person studied. Third, create a reasonable study schedule. Normally, students who do well on Step 1 also do well on the Step 2 CK. It might be best to model the same person for Step 1 and for the Step 2 CK if that person did well on the tests. Your study schedule should be based on the successful student's schedule but customized for you. Determine your own areas of weakness and strength (shelf scores are often good predictors of this), and adjust your schedule accordingly. Most important, the study schedule should be reasonable. An unrealistic schedule can make your daily goals impossible to accomplish, and if that happens, you won't cover everything you wished to cover. As always, avoid studying for too long at one time to avoid burnout.

The next step in preparing to study for the Step 2 CK is to obtain the proper study materials. Again, this is similar to Step 1 in that most students study through a combination of review books and question banks. As with Step 1, the best way to figure out which materials to use is to poll students who have already taken the test. They will be able to tell you which review books and question banks are worthwhile and which are not. Since question banks cost a fair amount of money and are large, students commonly use just one, though some do use two question banks, depending on their study schedule. Use caution when choosing review books; many students blindly pick the same series of review books they used for Step 1, but just because a company makes a good Step 1 review book doesn't mean that its Step 2 CK review book will be good.

Once you have made up your study schedule and collected your review materials, you've reached the penultimate step. It's time to start studying. As with studying for the Step 1, try your best to keep faithful to your study schedule while also taking care of your mental health.

As with any standardized test, the final step is to actually take the test. By now, the average medical student can be considered a professional test taker having taken the SAT, MCAT, and Step 1 and each time being told, "This is the most important test of your life." And each time that is more or less true. The difference this time is that no one will tell you the Step 2 CK is the most important test of your life. Certainly strive to do your best—especially if you're taking it toward the start of the fourth year. But all things considered, you'll feel far less pressure taking the Step 2 CK than you have felt taking any previous standardized test.

Despite feeling less pressure, make sure you're well rested in the days leading up to test day. It is not uncommon to be restless the night before, but being well rested in the days leading up to the exam will create a buffer against the possible sleep debt you might accrue due to pretest jitters. By now, the other specifics of the pretest ritual should be old hat. Get all your pretest documents in order, visit the test center in the days before the test if you don't know where it is, and pack snacks. Use your break time strategically. It's a good idea to take a short break every section or so to refuel and refocus—trying to do too many sections without taking a break may result in a loss of concentration and a poorer score. Lastly, many students will rush through the last section of the test thinking, *I just want to be done!* But it makes no sense to have a "screw it" attitude after all your studying and hard work when you have just one section to go. Calm down, refocus, and treat the last section of the test just like any other section. After the test, congratulate yourself on its completion.

You've finished the last medical school test of any importance.

Summary

The Step 2 CK is a far easier and less stressful test than the Step 1. Although you can take it anytime during your fourth year, it may be advantageous to take it on the earlier side as it will be easier to study for, some residency programs won't consider your application complete until they have your Step 2 CK score, and getting it out of the way is a relief. The strategy you should use to study for the Step 2 CK should be very similar to the strategy used to study for Step 1: learn the material during your clinical rotations, copy a successful student's methods, create a reasonable personalized study schedule, obtain the proper study materials, start studying, gain familiarity with the testing center, and make sure you take breaks on test day and don't blow off the last section.

9 | The USMLE Step 2 CS

You knew you shouldn't have looked at your bank account last night. The knowledge that only a few hundred dollars remains between you and poverty causes a sickening feeling to arise in your stomach. "I probably shouldn't be thinking about this right now," you murmur to yourself as your foot gets a little heavier on the accelerator. Your GPS shows that you are only about ten minutes away from the hallowed Atlanta testing center. You're fortunate that you happen to have an uncle who lives in Atlanta because the burden of an extra night in a hotel room would have been almost too much to bear. One of your medical school buddies was not so lucky: he waited too long to schedule his exam and ended up having to take it in Houston. The fact that he had to book a flight, rent a car, and get a hotel room shouldn't make you feel any better, but yet it does. Well, you don't exactly feel bad for him; he was told multiple times to register early and was just too lazy to do so.

You are finding it increasingly hard not to be frustrated with the inconvenience of this exam as you pull up to the testing center—a nondescript medium-sized office building on the outskirts of Atlanta. If it weren't for the limited exam locations, the chaos of your fourth-year schedule, and the ridiculous cost of this test, taking this exam probably wouldn't bother you so much. On the bright side, the fact that you studied only a handful of hours for this exam is almost laughable when compared to the studying you did for the Step 1. You take relief in knowing that it's almost unheard of to fail this exam. With a deep sigh, you step out of your car into the pleasantly warm fall air and start making your way toward the building. Clad in your white coat, shirt, and tie, you feel like something is missing because you dumped practically a year's worth of papers, pens, and other miscellaneous objects from your white coat pockets last night. The rules were very clear about bringing only a stethoscope.

It's not hard to figure out where to go as multiple other white coats are filing into the building ahead of you. The testing lobby is as nondescript as the building's exterior: a large square room with a desk on one end and seats all along the periphery. Almost every seat is already occupied by the time you get there. After you quickly check in and sit silently about twenty minutes, trying not to stare at the other examinees, one of the proctors enters the room and calls for attention. She motions for everyone to follow her to the testing rooms and begins to explain the details of the exam. You try to hang on her every word, but she is only repeating what you already know.

A short while later you find yourself staring at "Exam Room 10" near the far end of a long hallway that is peppered with doors and computers. A glance to your left reveals an array of white coats, each standing in front of a numbered exam room, ready to meet a standardized patient. Soon your job will be to take a history and focused physical on twelve of such patients, and write a short note after each encounter on one of the hallway computers. Even though you generally like seeing patients in a clinical setting, you would rather not be here. You would rather be at home, a thousand dollars richer in the company of your friends and family.

As its name indicates, the USMLE Step 2 Clinical Skills (Step 2 CS) exam seeks to assess the clinical skills of the person taking the exam. Most medical schools require students to take this exam to graduate, and you must pass it to obtain your medical license. The test's assessment of clinical skills is broken down into three nebulous subcomponents: integrated clinical encounter, communication and interpersonal skills, and spoken English proficiency. The integrated clinical encounter score is determined by a checklist the standardized patient fills out about the physical exam performed and the quality of the written note as determined by trained physician raters. The communication and interpersonal skills section is scored by the standardized patient, who has a checklist of observable behaviors—from information gathering to emotional support. The spoken English proficiency subcomponent tests how well the student can speak English based on pronunciation errors, word choice errors, and the level of listening effort needed to understand the student. The truth is, none of this really matters.

The Step 2 CS is probably the first major test of a medical student's career that is strictly pass or fail. Each of the three subcomponents receives a pass or fail mark that contributes to the overall pass or fail grade. You must pass each subcomponent to pass the test. And because there are no numerical grades, one student's pass is equal to that of any other. As a result, this test likely has no influence on residency committee decisions (unless a student fails it). In fact, since the test takes two to three months to grade, most programs won't even have the results by the time they select students for interviews.

The Step 2 CS exam is a unique test that is formatted as follows: The student does a history and physical on multiple standardized patients (actors) and writes a brief note after each encounter. Usually this involves twelve patient encounters with fifteen minutes given to perform an H&P and ten minutes to write a note for each patient. Each standardized patient is in a separate exam room that resembles and contains all the equipment of a real-world exam room. A computer outside each exam room is where the student writes the note. At the end of the ten-minute note-writing period, students receive an instruction to switch, and each then moves to the next station. A couple of mandatory breaks are worked into the schedule, and on one of those breaks lunch is served.

Most native English speakers have no problem passing this test, which creates a low-stress situation. The major issue students have with this test is that it is inconvenient in a variety of ways. First, it is ridiculously expensive, costing over a thousand dollars. The fourth year, considering the costs of interviewing, doing away rotations, and taking the Step 2 CK (roughly half the price of the Step 2 CS) is already expensive, and this added cost comes at the worst possible time in a medical student's career. Second, the test is offered in just five locations, so unless you live in Atlanta, Chicago, Philadelphia, Houston, or Los Angeles, you'll have to travel to take the exam. In the most difficult scenario, students must buy a plane ticket, get a hotel room, and rent a car to take the test.

The availability of testing dates is also inconvenient. Every fourth-year medical student in the nation has to take this test, as do any foreign students or doctors who want to do their residency in the United States. Each testing center can accommodate only about twenty-four students at a time, though some centers offer a morning test and an afternoon test, so they can accommodate forty-eight students a day. Available dates fill up fast, and getting a convenient date can be a challenge.

My best advice is to sign up early and try to make the test conform to already existing travel plans. If you're lucky enough to live within driving distance of a center, you can take the test when it's most convenient. If you aren't, setting a date will be more complicated. The first half of the fourth year for many students is typified by living out of a suitcase, constantly traveling. Chances are that at some point during your journeys to away rotations or to visit home, you'll be close to a testing center, and this would be the best time to schedule the Step 2 CS. Trying to time the test to match interview dates is almost impossible since most interview dates aren't offered until later in the year, and by that time it's likely test center dates will be filled. Once you assess a convenient time to take the test, sign up immediately!

After you have figured out when and where you will take the test and how you are going to pay for it, you must prepare for it. Thankfully, this is the easiest step. The average native-English-speaking student usually studies only a handful of hours (fewer than ten). This is a welcome change from the weeks and weeks of time sacrificed to studying for every previously taken standardized test. The Step 2 CS is not a hard test to pass, and the average fourth-year medical student should be more than equipped to pass it with all the clinical skills learned in the previous three years. That said, it doesn't hurt to review what you've learned before taking it. Most students will read part of a Step 2 CS review book, usually one that they found for free. Some students may want to practice their clinical skills with friends—not necessary but sometimes helpful in calming nerves.

Most nonnative English speakers will have a more-than-sufficient clinical skill set to pass those aspects of the test, but the spoken English proficiency section can be a challenge. Errors in word choice and pronunciation will be held against such students, and since increasing language proficiency is no easy task, the best approach for nonnative English speakers worried that their language proficiency might not be up to par is to focus on word choice and pronunciation in medical-related language. The next step is to speak and practice English as much as possible prior to the test.

The last step is to take the exam. Obviously, you'll want to make sure all your paperwork is in order and know where the testing center is so that you can plan to arrive with more than enough time to spare. The dress code is typical for clinical work: shirt and tie for men, office-style attire for women, and a white coat for all. Take everything but a stethoscope out of the pockets of your white coat as the testing center provides everything else. Many centers will also have a limited number of extra white coats and stethoscopes for those students who forget, but you don't want to be one of those people. A piece of black duct tape will be placed over names, school affiliations, and any other identifying marks on the coats. Lunch is provided (the least they can do considering the exorbitant costs) so you won't need to bring snacks. And you will not have access to your belongings throughout the day; these will be locked up when you arrive and during the entire exam.

The testing center will give each test taker two pens and a clipboard with twelve pieces of numbered scrap paper. At the start of the exam, the test taker will see a short description of the clinical scenario pasted on the outside of the door. Be sure to read this description and note any important details. After you're done reading, proceed into the room and meet the standardized patient. Remember to introduce yourself, wash your hands, and ask if the patient is comfortable before beginning to take a history. Proceed to take a full history, meaning the chief complaint, history of the present illness, past medical history, surgical history, medications, allergies, family history, social history, and review of systems (general questions about each organ system meant to identify disease or dysfunction). Some students worry about how they'll complete a full history and focused physical in fifteen minutes, but remember, the standardized patient, unlike a real patient, will help you fly through the questions, and most aspects of the history will be negative. After you've taken the history, remember to summarize the relevant parts of it for the standardized patient to make sure you have been accurate. While the physical exam is a focused one, you'll still want to be thorough. If you're unsure about whether to do a certain part of the physical exam, go ahead and do it as long as time permits, as points will not be subtracted for extraneous physical exam maneuvers. To end the patient encounter, explain your findings—what you think the problem is and how you'll proceed—to the patient.

If you finish the H&P in less than fifteen minutes, you can proceed immediately to write the note on the computer outside the exam room. Any extra time you gain from finishing the H&P early is added to the time allowed to write the note. In other words, if you finish the H&P in eleven minutes you'll have fourteen minutes to write the note instead of the standard ten. The note is not a blank page welcoming you to write whatever you want. Rather, you'll have a space to write history findings, physical exam findings, three differential diagnoses, the history and physical exam findings that support each diagnosis, and tests that would be ordered. You need not include any justification for selecting one diagnosis over another; just include the history and physical exam findings that support each diagnosis. Once you're done writing the note, hit Submit and wait for the proctors to tell everyone to switch stations. This process repeats itself eleven more times, with two breaks built into the day.

Summary

Despite its inconvenience and expense, this standardized test is probably the easiest you'll ever take. You'll need to do only minimal studying to prepare for it, but do make sure to arrange to take it at a convenient time. Then pass it and forget about it.

10 | The Fourth Year in a Nutshell

The light flooding into your room sends the signal that it will be time to get up soon. Try as you might, you aren't capable of sleeping until your alarm goes off this morning. It's 7:46 a.m., and you don't have to be at the hospital for your radiology elective until about 9:00. Despite the fact that you slept almost eight hours last night, you're feeling sluggish. It's not that you're tired; rather, it's that you no longer have the motivation. The thought that you will probably get out by noon helps somewhat—a three-hour workday is reasonable. Still, finding the drive to get up and dressed is challenging.

The last time you wore a tie was three weeks ago during your final residency interview. The thought of wrapping a constricting piece of silk around your neck now is almost laughable. In fact, it's been almost a week since you shaved or styled your hair, and your current wardrobe consists almost completely of scrubs. Thankfully, you have stolen enough pairs over the past two years to go a couple of weeks without doing laundry. Clearly, these days you aren't trying to impress anyone.

You finally get up and dress. As you're walking to the car, you think how nice it is to see sunlight. Just a few months ago you were waking up before the sun rose and coming home after it had set. You remember how tired you felt as you pushed an eighty-hour workweek during your subinternships and away rotations. The earlier part of the fourth year contrasts starkly to life now. Getting up at 8:00 and working just three hours with no weekend or on-call days is like taking a vacation. The fact that you have already applied and interviewed for residency lessens the stress of this radiology rotation still more. You only have to pass; and to pass, all you have to do is show up a few hours a day—there are no tests or assignments.

One downside to having to arrive somewhere at a "normal" time is the traffic, and this morning you find yourself hopelessly stuck in traffic and knowing you'll be late. A few months ago this would have caused utter dread and panic, but now you couldn't care less. At precisely 9:17, you roll into the radiology room to no reaction from either the attendings or the residents. They barely notice you're there. In fact, you aren't even the last fourth-year student to show up. The residents and attendings know you aren't going to specialize in radiology. They know you're not interested in radiology at all and you took this elective because it has the reputation of being easy. There are no secrets anymore. After two uneventful hours, one of the residents says that you can go home if you want to. You are quick to respond, "See you later," and by 11:33 you're out the door. It might be a little early for lunch, but what else have you got to do?

Of course you could go anywhere for lunch—you certainly have the time—but out of pure convenience and laziness you decide to eat at the hospital cafeteria. *It's always nice to beat the lunch crowd*, you think as you grab a tray and inhale that familiar hospital cafeteria smell that can't be replicated anywhere else. The cafeteria staff is busy gearing up for the onslaught of scrubs and white coats that will soon storm in. The low-priced, mediocre sandwich causes you to quickly enter a food coma.

When you finish eating, you still don't feel like moving, but after spending a few minutes staring at the wall, you finally gather the momentum to stand. But before you can get to your feet, your friend Rob spots you and heads over. It looks like he has already eaten half his meal while waiting in line to pay. As your eyes lock,

Rob shakes his head in a slow, depressed manner. "Oh, you must be on your medicine sub-I. How's that going?" you ask casually as he reaches your table and sits down. He continues to shake his head and says in a too loud voice, "Wonderful, just wonderful!" Rob has been keen on general surgery since day one of medical school. Unfortunately, he was one of the last students in line to pick out a fourth-year schedule, and this meant he got stuck with one of the harder medical subinternships. He has clearly been forced out of fourth-year retirement into an intense rotation he doesn't like. Still too loud, he complains, "I have to work this weekend." Despite the fact that you aren't going into psychiatry, Rob proceeds to recite his problems. A few minutes later, he chugs the rest of his soda, shuffles his garbage back on his tray, and leaves just as he arrived—chewing and complaining.

Upon exiting the cafeteria, you reminisce about the hours of sleep you lost and the many meals you missed during the hardest of your fourth-year rotations. Back then you were more motivated. When you reach home, you recall the days you crossed the threshold cringing at the thought of the many hours of study that lay ahead. Those days are long gone, and now with nothing you have to do, you decide a nap is in order. There's no point in setting an alarm because when you get up truly doesn't matter.

Lying in bed without being tired causes all your thoughts to rise to the surface. *I really should be more relaxed than I am*, you think. Dreams of the easy lifestyle you have now are what kept you going during the barrage of subinternships that you suffered through earlier in the year. The truth is that although your life now is awesome, something is bothering you. Something won't let you relax. Just then, a thought rises from the depths of your mind and pierces its way right to the forefront. *What if I don't get matched to where I want to go? What if I don't match at all?* When you consider the complexity of reapplying for residency, this thought becomes still more harrowing. A couple of months ago, the thought of match day barely existed. You were simply concerned with finishing your subinternships and getting on the interview trail. Now that life has calmed down, with every passing day the anxiety of match day increases. At times the anxiety almost boils over into hysteria.

One more month and I will finally know, for better or for worse.

The Unique Fourth Year

The fourth year of medical school is unique. The first three years are typified by near-constant studying, with a test always looming and a constant barrage of material to learn. During the fourth year, test taking is minimal (besides the Step 2s, of course). Although some fourth-year rotations do have tests, the grades are either pass or fail and they almost don't matter. Also, assignments barely exist. You could probably make it through the entire year without ever cracking a book.

Besides the lack of studying and test taking, fourth-year rotations feel different from third-year rotations. They fall into one of three categories: insanely easy, brutally hard, or extremely annoying. Rotations that are easy are thus because the grades don't matter and most students don't feel the need to impress anyone by working extra hard or staying late. This means the hours are good. Easy rotations usually don't have any assignments or tests, so once you're back home, there's nothing you must do, which means the stress level is lower. The brutally hard fourth-year rotations normally require an enormous amount of your time. These are usually away rotations and subinternships, and although they usually have no assignments or tests, the sheer effort required to try to impress everyone all the time takes its toll (see chapter 11, "The Away Rotation"). A subinternship can be tough if you're actually "part of the medical team," with nearly the same responsibilities as an intern and therefore similar work hours. The annoying rotations are the required non-sub-I rotations no student would ever think of taking unless he or she were going into that field. Frequently, these rotations have special parameters set up to prevent students from skating by and leaving early, and these rotations require students to be there a set number of hours, even if there's nothing to do. As in prison, the only way out is to do your time.

The fourth year also involves a great deal of travel and time spent away from your home institution. Between all the residency interviews and away rotations, many students spend months away from home. Of course, if you decide to do no away rotations, you'll be home more, but because most schools give one to two months of unscheduled free time for interviewing and taking the Step 2s, the time away can still be substantial. Needless to say, the average fourth-year medical student puts a lot of miles on the car, becomes accustomed to living out of a suitcase, and spends a lot of time in airports.

One of the most important differences between the fourth year and the rest of medical school is that you can actually choose your schedule! The first two years of medical school are set in stone, while the third year has a little bit of play as you'll get some say in choosing the order of your rotations—which can be likened to doing the events of a decathlon in whichever order one desires. Still, at the end of the competition, you'll have to have completed all the events. The fourth year of medical school is more like ordering a burrito bowl—you'll include meat (or extra veggies), some kind of rice, and some beans, and after that, anything goes.

However, having the freedom to choose a schedule is a double-edged sword. On the one hand, you're free to select rotations you're interested in and want to take. On the other hand, you have to grapple with getting the home rotations you want, scheduling your away rotations, making sure you take all the required rotations, and finding enough free time to interview and take the Step 2s. The fourth year involves a level of complexity not present in the previous three years, and choosing your schedule will dictate the rhythm of the year. Some students will end up with much harder rotations than will others. Some will have to ask for time off from a rotation to interview, while others with unscheduled time will simply pack up and go. Some may even have the unfortunate luck of having to take a rotation after graduation! Creating a reasonable schedule will make a world of difference in your life during the fourth year. All things considered, creating a good schedule is the first and most important part of the year.

So how do you create your year? Luck is the first component. Having a lot of luck equates to being first in line to choose rotations. Each school is different, but most have a random selection process. Some schools simply reverse the third-year choosing order. Whatever the case, those at the front of the line will get to mold their schedules the way they please, while those at the back will be forced to take the scraps. Those who choose last will probably end up having to take required rotations during inconvenient times and won't be able to schedule free time during interview season. This can create a hardship if your rotation lets you take off only a few days for interviewing. You won't have to miss interviews but you'll have to talk to the course coordinator and work something out.

The Schedule

Choosing a fourth-year schedule normally takes place toward the end of the third year. Most schools give incoming fourth-year students a fair amount of warning before the day approaches, so use this time to figure out an ideal schedule as well as backups. First, find out the most important courses to take for your desired specialty. Some specialties may request that you do specific rotations to meet key faculty and to receive necessary letters of recommendation. The best way to know which rotations to take for a given specialty is to ask the course coordinator or program director directly. It is also a good idea to schedule these rotations as soon as possible to provide plenty of time to gather your recommendation letters and to make important connections before the interview process begins. Most students schedule these rotations for the very start of the academic year.

Next, figure out your away rotations. Not everyone has to do away rotations, and some do more than others. Choosing away rotations is discussed in greater detail in chapter 11, "The Away Rotation," because it is a complex process. Suffice it to say that the main point of away rotations is to increase your chances of being matched to a given institution. Doing away rotations is pointless after interview season, and next to impossible during interview season. So the primary question is whether to schedule them before your specialty-specific home rotations or afterward.

The advantage of scheduling home rotations first is that they will help you prepare for the types of challenges that lay ahead of you. You'll have had no exposure to some specialties before the fourth year, which means you might start a specialty knowing almost nothing about it. Doing your home rotations first will provide you the crash-course experience you'll need and will allow you to appear to be more knowledgeable in the future. It will also give you plenty of time to obtain letters of recommendation, and doing an away rotation after your home rotations has the advantage of leaving a fresh impression with the away institution just before interview season starts. Doing an away rotation six months before interview season could result in your having been forgotten by the time interview season rolls around—though if you do well, you'll be remembered.

One disadvantage is associated with doing home rotations first. You might have a harder time obtaining letters of recommendation from away rotations as you'll need to use the Electronic Residency Application Service, and the application must be submitted early in the year. While you don't have to obtain letters of recommendation from your away rotations, doing so can strengthen your application by providing a diverse array of letter writers. Doing your away rotations first will make it easier to get letters of recommendation from important faculty at other institutions—though you do run the risk of appearing to be (and actually being) clueless at the start of the rotation. If your top choice is your home institution, doing an away rotation first might make sense, but make sure you have enough time to get the required letters of recommendation from home faculty. Regardless of your desires, your personal scheduling conflicts may mean that there is only one possible way to order your rotations. In the end, you'll have to do your best within your own constraints.

Once you have hammered out your specialty-specific home and away rotations, the next step is to figure out when to place your unscheduled time, time designed to be used for interviewing and taking the Step 2s.

Placing your unscheduled time in interview season will lower your costs and make your life easier (discussed in more detail in chapter 12, "The Residency Interview").

Deciding when to take the Step 2s is also challenging and is discussed thoroughly in the previous two chapters. Simply put, the Step 2 CK is easiest to study for at the end of the third year when the knowledge is still fresh and you're still motivated. One possible downside of taking the Step 2 CK early is that residency programs will be able to see your grade, but some residency programs are beginning to require Step 2 CK grades before they even consider an application. Taking the Step 2 CK on the earlier side is probably most prudent, but you must find the most convenient time for you. The Step 2 CS requires almost no studying but may require some travel, so as discussed in the previous chapter, you'll want to plan carefully. Some fourth-year students complain about having to travel to take the Step 2 CS after they have already traveled for interviewing. Regardless of when you choose to take these tests, you should pay for and schedule them right away as testing dates often fill up months in advance.

The last step in creating a fourth-year schedule is to figure out the remaining required courses you'll need to take and to fit these in however possible. Some medical schools have many required fourth-year rotations, while others have almost none. Sometimes only one course is available for a required rotation, but more often, a few different options are available for a given requirement. Deciding on the course you want to take can be hard since reading a two-paragraph synopsis of that course in an elective manual is rarely helpful. Some courses that sound interesting turn out to be strenuous and unenjoyable. It's wise to ask outgoing fourth-year students which courses they recommend—which ones are worthwhile, which are easy, and which should be avoided. It is not a bad idea to err on the side of taking easier required courses as a "break" from the more strenuous subinternships and away rotations. Scheduling too many intense rotations in a row can lead to burnout, especially when taking into account the decreased motivation of fourth-year students during the later parts of the year.

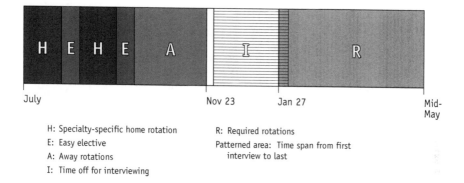

H: Specialty-specific home rotation
E: Easy elective
A: Away rotations
I: Time off for interviewing

R: Required rotations
Patterned area: Time span from first
  interview to last

Figure 10.1 My fourth-year schedule

Although creating a fourth-year schedule can be stressful, you should definitely create an ideal schedule and also backups. Specialty-specific home rotations and away rotations should take priority. Of course, you must complete all the required rotations to graduate, so this is a delicate dance. Ultimately, you'll have to work the best you can with what you are given. I was toward the middle of my fourth-year lottery and ended up with a great schedule so that my personal fourth-year schedule looked like figure 10.1. (I ended up taking the Step 2 CK in the short time between the third and fourth years.)

Once you've created your fourth-year schedule, let out a big sigh of relief. With the majority of fourth-year courses being pass or fail, doing well on a rotation means something slightly different than it did during the third year. The main goal of fourth-year rotations is to impress the faculty and residents to secure a residency spot or obtain letters of recommendation. This is necessary only during the beginning of the year on your specialty-specific home and away rotations and is discussed in greater detail in chapter 11, "The Away Rotation." Suffice it to say for now that good third-year medical students won't have a problem doing well in their fourth-year rotations.

Residency Applications

Besides tough subinternships, away rotations, and scheduling, the next sizeable hurdle in the fourth year is applying for residency. Fortunately, all applications are submitted electronically using the Electronic Residency Application Service. You'll thus be required to complete just one online application, which you can send everywhere! Using the ERAS application, you'll have the ability to list and explain any activity, award, publication, work experience, volunteer experience, research, hobby, or other information you wish to share. Also included in the application are your Step scores, a professional photo, letters of recommendation, and a personal statement. Try to include everything you've done or participated in as well as any interesting hobbies, but avoid including items about which you aren't knowledgeable or cannot explain clearly. During your interview you'll want to be able to speak intelligently about every topic raised.

Inputting your résumé isn't difficult, and releasing your Step scores is as easy as the click of a button, but other aspects of the application can be trickier. The professional photo can be a pain—you'll need to make an appointment with a school or private photographer. This is the picture residency programs will see when they read your application, so you'll want to dress professionally and men will want to be clean shaven. Getting the photo retouched doesn't hurt either.

The personal statement is usually about one page single spaced, although you can make it shorter or longer. Residency program directors read hundreds of applications and may not have the patience to read a lengthy account of your life, so keep in mind that a good personal statement will explain in a creative and moving way why you want to go into a given field. Try your best to make the read enjoyable. Showing rough drafts to your advising dean may be wise. Submitting the rough drafts to a great writer friend is also a good idea. You might want to write more than one statement and choose which ones to submit to specific institutions—this can be especially helpful if you're applying to more than one specialty. A personal statement won't make or break your application, but it can prove to be a springboard to conversation in your interview.

Every residency program will also require letters of recommendation. Obtaining a letter of recommendation in medical school is usually easier than obtaining one in college since you're likely to have closer relationships with your attendings than you did with your college professors. Still, getting an attending to actually write the letter can be like pulling teeth. Some will do it right away, but others will need to be continuously coaxed. Asking for your letter before the end of a rotation is ideal. You can ask for the letter earlier if the ERAS opening date is rapidly approaching.

You may wonder how you can get the attending to write a letter for you. The easy answer is simply to ask. Even if an attending knows you well, she still might be at a loss for details to write about, so be sure to give any recommendation writer your résumé, personal statement, Step scores, photo, and anything else you'd like her to know about you. Give the letter writer an ERAS cover sheet with the specifics of what should be contained in the letter, including your AMCAS (American Medical College Application Service) identification number, the statement that you have waived your right to read the letter, and a few other pertinent details that can be found on the ERAS website.

Most institutions require at least three letters but will let a student submit four, so it is wise to obtain at least four letters. You might want to obtain more and then pick the best ones. Of course, the question arises, How do you know which letters are good if you can't read them? This is where your advising dean comes in. The applicant may not be able to read the letters, but the advising dean can. No doubt the dean has read hundreds, possibly even thousands, of letters over the course of a career and will easily be able to tell which letters are worth using and which aren't. Also, the advising dean can act as a safeguard against the rare negative letter. Most attendings won't write a negative review of someone since the results could be devastating for the applicant. Still, having your advising dean screen the letters of recommendation will eliminate that possibility.

The hardest question to answer concerning letters of recommendation is, Whom should I ask? The simple answer is, Ask whoever will write a good one. Obviously, this has many caveats, but it comes down to who will write the best letter. Asking attendings in your desired specialty is wise, although not every single letter needs to be from that specialty. If an attending volunteers to write you a letter, definitely take him up on it. It will likely be good—even if that attending is not in your specialty. Many residency programs require a letter from the department chair of your desired specialty, and some programs also require a letter from the program director. You'll thus have to ask these people for letters of recommendation. Also included in every application is the dean's letter, in essence a compilation of all your third-year clerkship narratives. This, however, does not count as a letter of recommendation.

Finding an attending who will write a good letter involves three elements. First, the better an attending knows you and the more that attending likes you, the better the letter will be. Second, if an attending is a naturally gifted writer who has the tendency to embellish her writing, the letter will most likely be very good. This attending will write more than one page, detailing all the fabulous work you've done and exclaiming about how lucky any residency program would be to have you. Third, if an attending is well known in his respective medical community (for positive reasons), his name alone will add weight to the letter. If all three aspects are positive, we're left with a famous attending who knows you very well, likes you, and is a gifted writer. This letter will be ideal.

Of course, most of the time all three aspects will not be positive. A letter writer may be famous but not know you well and not be a great writer. Or an attending may be a great writer who knows you well but is not well known in the medical community. The one aspect that trumps all others is being a good writer. When it comes to recommendation writing, "good" has more to do with the level of embellishment than elegance of language. Writing elegantly is nice, but if an attending writes five elegant sentences, the letter will not be nearly as good as a page and a half of plain language that makes sure you sound good, even if the writer doesn't know you well. An attending who usually writes five-sentence letters of recommendation is not the best person to ask. Even if this person is your friend, in the best case he'll write seven sentences instead of five. Generally, a longer letter says more about how much the letter writer cares. The same goes for famous people. Residency programs can learn little about you in a five-sentence letter from someone famous. This type of letter only reveals the fact that you asked a famous attending for a letter and the attending didn't say no.

You might think that if an attending has written a book, she'll probably have no problem writing a page or two for you. This isn't always true, of course, and an attending who is a prolific writer might still write a lousy letter. The best way to find out which attendings write good letters is to ask either the medical school coordinator, your advising dean, or any others in the medical school who are responsible for processing letters of recommendation. With some coaxing, they may tell you which attendings generally write good letters.

In the end, this is a tricky business. You can't go wrong choosing someone known for writing good letters, even if that person doesn't know you well. Obviously, choosing a letter writer who knows you very well or someone who is famous can only help, and it's wise to ask your advising dean to screen your letters. During my application process I obtained a letter from a famous attending I wound up not using because it didn't say much about me. Having a surplus of letters will give you options.

Selection of Programs

When you have completed your application, the penultimate step is to choose which programs to apply to. ERAS makes this easy in that you can apply to every program that participates in the matching program simply by checking an extra box. Of course, only a certain number of programs are included in the initial application fee; each additional one costs extra. The more places you apply to, the more expensive the application process will be. If you're applying to a lot of programs, costs will quickly mount.

The strength of your application and the competitiveness of the desired specialty will guide the number of programs to which you ought to apply. A strong applicant can probably get away with applying to fewer places than can a weaker one. Also, if a specialty is difficult to be matched to, you should probably apply to more places. The only thing you have to lose by applying to many places is money, and at this juncture, even if you have little money, it's unwise to nickel-and-dime yourself. In other words, with all the thousands upon thousands of dollars you've already invested in your medical education, skimping on a few extra hundred dollars of application fees makes no sense. I'm sure you'd rather have more interviews and slightly less money than the opposite. The best way to get an idea of how many places you should apply to is to ask multiple interns and residents in the desired specialty how many places they applied to. It's not a bad idea to ask friends who are trying to be matched to the given field as well. For those trying to go into supercompetitive specialties, it's not uncommon to apply to seventy or more programs. Those trying to go into less-competitive fields might apply to half that number.

Picking out the specific places is not as hard as it seems. Most competitive specialties have fewer programs and spots than less-competitive specialties. Commonly, an applicant will go state by state and apply to every program in desirable areas. Those going into less-competitive specialties will have to be more selective as they have more programs to choose from; at the same time, they're probably applying to fewer places. Most applicants end up choosing programs based on a combination of location, name recognition, and type of hospital setting (community or university). Remember, the goal of applying to a program is to get an interview, and if you do get one, you can decide then how badly you want to go there. In the end, sending away an extra application is harmless.

When applying to residencies, you'll want to be aware that a few programs now require secondary applications. Sometimes the secondary is as simple as filling out an extra page of information or sending a copy of your MCAT scores. Sometimes the secondary will require the applicant to write an essay about why he wants to go to the program in question. (Thankfully, only one program out of the 75 I applied to asked me for this.) Possibly the worst type of secondary is the supplemental letter of recommendation form. Why some programs want this is beyond me, but they require all your letter writers to answer a few quick questions about you. Getting these filled out can be almost as difficult as obtaining the initial letter of recommendation, so it's a good idea to look at every program and see if it requires any sort of secondary before you send in your application. This will help you avoid wasting money on applications you might ultimately decide not to complete.

You won't be able to physically send out your application until the day that the ERAS opens for the school year, usually sometime in mid-September. However, you will still be able to do all the previous steps and have your application ready beforehand. Sending an application on the first day means that it has to be completed before that date, so make every effort to complete your application before the submission date. The last step in completing the ERAS application is to pay the fee and send the application out. At this point, residency programs will be able to download and start viewing your application.

Once the ERAS application is out, you'll wait for the interview offers to start rolling in. Interview season is a necessary evil that complicates your fourth year. In chapter 12, "The Residency Interview," I cover this topic more thoroughly, but in short, know that while the program is interviewing you, you should also be interviewing the program. Of course, you'll want to do well in your interview, but you should also be trying to decide if the program in question is right for you. Ask the program's residents and attendings every question you can think of. Students who have rotated at the program are also an excellent source of knowledge, and you can ask them questions that you might not want to ask a resident—for example, Are the residents happy here? How many hours do the residents actually work?

You might not know ahead of time what you want in a residency program. The fact that all residency programs have to meet minimum requirements to stay accredited means that no matter where you go, you'll likely receive a good education as long as you are willing to receive it. However, you'll want to determine which type of program has the best learning environment for you. Figuring this out is not always easy, but one way to get an idea of what you want is to rotate through different types of hospitals, which will allow you to compare different environments. The more hospitals you rotate through, the better your perspective will be on what you want and need. Some medical schools have just one hospital, but you can expand your experience through away rotations. Another way to figure out what type of program you're looking for is to ask the current residents in your desired specialty what they like and dislike about the program they are in. This might shed some light on topics you have not yet even considered.

With luck, by the time the interview season starts, you'll have figured out what you're looking for in a residency program. Since different people are looking for different things in residencies, there is no magic formula for finding the perfect program. Some may prefer a large academic program, while others would be content in a smaller community-style program. One is not necessarily better than the other. Some applicants will choose a program based on location, name recognition, or quality of fellowship placements. You need to know what you're looking for so you can ask appropriate questions during your interviews. This will help you create a well-thought-out rank list.

If you don't know what you want, you might be swayed by minutiae such as a nice fitness center or a generous meal plan. Never select your program based on such immaterial items as these will be completely over-shadowed by the general experience in the hospital. The best fitness center in the world and all the free meals you desire won't make up for working in a miserable environment. Also beware of programs that talk only about the benefits of living in their area. Some programs show pictures of the residents on the beach or on a hiking trail or on some mystical adventure but never mention anything about the hospital. That's a bad sign as it probably means that working in that hospital is miserable.

Unfortunately, knowing what you want in a residency program is only half the battle. The other half is figuring out which programs offer the aspects you seek. This is less of a problem at the institutions where you have rotated since a rotation provides you firsthand knowledge about the program. The difficulty lies in gaining information about the places you visit only on interview day. Even if you talk to the rotators, residents, and faculty, and they each answer a million questions, getting a good feel for a program in one day is tough. Without working at an institution, you probably won't know what it is really like, and it is highly impractical to take a second look at every place you interviewed. Take a second look only if you're having a hard time choosing between two programs for your number one selection.

Since obtaining firsthand knowledge of every program is impossible, students are often forced to go with their gut feeling, the overall impression about a program. While facts and data about a program are comforting, do not ignore your gut feeling. If a program gives you bad vibes, don't rank it high. Conversely, if a program gives you good feelings, don't ignore those feelings.

Celebration

After you've survived the madness that is interview season, the next step is to celebrate. You'll spend a lot of the fourth year trying to impress other people and working to make yourself look good. The process is draining, forcing you to monitor everything you do and say. After interview season, the situation is the opposite: the average fourth-year medical student isn't trying to impress anybody! But before you let yourself go, you need to complete one more important task. You must create your rank list, and to do this, it's important to know how the whole match and rank business actually works.

When applying to college and medical school, you receive rejections and acceptances. Those who receive a lot of acceptances can choose where they would like to matriculate. The match system that residency programs use is quite different. As the applicant, you'll create a list of programs you would like to go to, in the order of your preference, and input that list into the National Resident Matching Program (NRMP). Residency programs do the same, except their lists contain the names of the applicants they have interviewed in the order in which they want them. All the applicant and residency program lists are then inputted into a computer, which spits out a list of where everyone will go. Once the computer has made up its mind, there is no changing it. The program to which you're matched is the one you'll have to go to.

Sometimes the computer won't find a place for an applicant—if you're one of those applicants, you're considered unmatched. Similarly, the computer will sometimes not fill all the spots for specific specialties in certain programs. Unmatched applicants then have a chance to apply for those unmatched residency spots through an online system similar to the NRMP called the Supplemental Offer and Acceptance Program (SOAP). The same organization that operates the NRMP operates SOAP, which has three rounds, meaning that if you are not matched to an unmatched spot the first time around, you'll still have two more chances to be matched to any leftover spots through the same process. Do not preoccupy yourself with SOAP; the vast majority of applicants are matched the first time around.

As you apply to residency, you'll likely have to explain the match over and over again to all your relatives. The question that always follows is, How does the computer know where to put everybody? While the precise algorithm of the NRMP is unknown, the NRMP has provided a general outline. The computer looks at an applicant's rank list and tries to match that applicant with her number one program. If the program has unfilled spots, the NRMP will tentatively place the applicant there. If all the spots are already tentatively filled by other applicants, two possibilities are looked at. First, if the applicant in question is ranked higher by the program than another applicant who is taking up a tentative spot, the applicant in question will kick the lower-ranked applicant out of the spot and take his place. Second, if all the other applicants are ranked higher than the applicant in question, she cannot be matched at this program and the computer will start the process all over again with the applicant's second choice. If no empty spot is available and the applicant cannot kick out anyone at her number two program, the computer will continue this process by moving down the applicant's rank list until it finds her a tentative spot. Of course, the applicant is always in danger of being kicked out of the spot by someone who is ranked higher. After every applicant has been considered, the match is finished. Every tentative spot becomes permanent at that point. The NRMP provides some great examples of how this whole process works on its website (http://www.nrmp.org/).

The truth is that you need not know the details of the match algorithm, you only need to know that the computer will make every effort to match you with your highest-ranked program. Some applicants incorrectly believe that they should rank a program as number one because the program gave them the impression that it ranked them high. First, take every promise a program makes with a grain of salt, and second, even if the promise is true and the program does rank you high, your rank list should not change. If a program ranks an applicant as number one, and the applicant ranks the program number twelve, the possibility exists for the computer to kick out anyone who is tentatively matched into a spot in that program, even if the person occupying the spot listed the program as his number one. The only way the applicant would be matched there is if the computer could not find her a spot at her first eleven places. So be sure to rank programs based on your personal preference.

Your Rank List

How do you create your rank list? Ideally, you would rank programs based on how happy you would be to be matched to them. Use the knowledge you have acquired about the programs and your gut feeling to make these decisions. It's usually easy to figure out the programs that will be at the top and bottom of your list, while filling in the middle part of the rank list, especially when two places seem about equal, is more difficult. In these instances, think about which places you would feel happiest. If you dislike a program, you have the option of not even putting it on your rank list, eliminating any possibility of being matched there. Do this only if you would rather not be matched at all than attend residency at the undesirable program. For highly competitive specialties, after a failed first attempt, matching becomes much harder, so you should rank every program. If you have had many interviews and you're applying to a less-competitive specialty, it may make more sense to not rank a less desirable program.

After you have created your rank list, you'll have to submit it to the NRMP to be included in the match. Those who fail to submit their rank list by the given deadline will not be included in the match. You will still have the ability to change your rank list before the deadline if you so desire, but you should submit at least a preliminary list well beforehand in case the computer system crashes. Once you have created a well-thought-out rank list, resist the impulse to change it at the last minute. Impulsive decisions often are not based on logic, and you may later regret a rash decision.

After submitting your rank list, you'll await match day. This often arouses much anxiety; thinking about the uncertainty of your future can be nerve-racking. At some medical schools, match day anxiety is only exacerbated by match day ceremonies that consist of all students opening up their match envelopes at the same time. Other schools call individuals up to a stage to read their results. As match day approaches, it is normal to feel some anxiety.

A few days before match day, you will receive an e-mail from the NRMP letting you know whether or not you have been matched. This day can be even more anxiety provoking than match day itself, especially if you're going into a competitive specialty; in this case, not being matched is a possibility. The thought *What if I don't match?* can keep you up at night, but you should resist worrying about matching because worrying won't change anything. Once you've submitted your list, the die is cast. Deciding what to do if you aren't matched is complicated since the situation is different for each individual. Your specialty may have no unmatched spots, and if this is the case, talking with your advising deans is recommended. They will help you figure out a plan. Most schools have a support network set up for those who are not matched.

Match day itself is a unique experience, as in a matter of seconds the uncertainty about your future dissolves. The fact that this is happening for many students at the same time makes the experience that much crazier. For those are who matched with their top choices, the day is joyful, while for those who wind up somewhere they thought they wouldn't, there may be surprise. Those who wind up matched with a place they didn't wish to go might be depressed, though these will be a small minority since most people wind up somewhere they would like to be. Besides, everyone ought to take solace in the proverb I once heard from a resident: "You match where you fit in best, whether you like it or not." Sometimes things happen for a reason. So regardless of the outcome, take the opportunity to celebrate with your friends on this unique day.

After match day celebrations are over, you will probably still have some rotations left to complete, the last step in receiving your doctor of medicine degree. Work hard not to fail these rotations, despite the fact that the motivation to do a good job once match day passes is next to nil. A colleague of mine who was matched with a very competitive specialty failed one of these rotations and ended up spending an extra month after graduation making it up! The end of the fourth year can feel very much like the end of high school. Even the most motivated medical student's desire to do well becomes replaced with the desire simply to pass and leave early. Those who were able to schedule easy rotations for the end of their fourth year now reap the benefits. Those who didn't might struggle through a tough rotation. Most attendings and residents are aware of the fourth year psyche and will give students a break. Other attendings and residents are less aware of the mind-set and will insist that you work. Working with an attending or resident who doesn't understand the fourth-year student mentality can be frustrating, but resist the urge to start fights over trivial matters. The last thing you want to do is make trouble for yourself just as you're about to graduate.

Summary

The fourth year of medical school is unique. At times you'll feel you're on an emotional roller coaster because the application process is both exciting and exhausting. As you near the end, take time to reflect on all the hard work you've done and the astonishing number of experiences you've had and the tremendous amount of knowledge you have acquired.

The gains are so monumental that you'll likely have difficulty imagining how little you knew when you began.

You'll learn so much more by the end of residency that it's mind boggling, but remember, before you finish residency, you have to start it. We've all heard stories about what is in store, but instead of worrying, experience the anticipatory excitement of all the new knowledge and skills ahead of you. By the end of your fourth year, you will be more than ready to take the next step in your education, but don't forget to enjoy your free time after graduation.

11 | The Away Rotation

It takes only a few seconds for the pleasant melody of your phone to wake you from what might end up being the best night's rest that you will get over the next four weeks. The mellow tone causes much less stress than did the wretched beeping sound of your old alarm clock. You quickly silence the ring and then turn off the old plug-in clock that is set to ring in ten more minutes. You realize that setting two alarm clocks might seem excessive, but if it prevents you from waking up in the middle of the night worrying about accidentally sleeping in, it's worth the extra effort. The idea is to get as much sleep as possible during those precious moments before work.

It's 5:47 a.m., and you don't have to be in until 7:00 to 7:30, when you'll go through administrative paperwork. Of course, this means that you will try to get there at 6:50 because you're trying to make that important good first impression. This being your third away rotation, you feel as if you've been making first impressions for months now. Almost every day you have a new resident to work with, a new attending to meet. And every day you strive to make the best impression you can because it might be the only day you work with those individuals. They will judge you, the rotator, based on whatever little time they spend with you, and one of them might just be the person most important in ranking you for the match.

It's still dark outside, and you realize that the inside tempera-ture is a little too cool for you to be wearing as little as you are.

You quickly dig through the dresser drawers you moved your stuff into last night. When you open the closet, you feel a strange jolt as you recognize that only a fourth of the clothes there are yours and the rest are those of a woman you've never met. You're staying with your girlfriend's mother's friend from the neighborhood your girlfriend lived in fifteen years ago. Stranger still, you're staying in the room of your girlfriend's childhood friend who is currently out of the country. You chose this place because you'd rather live somewhere that feels like home than in a lonely hotel room. The family was nice enough to offer you lodging for free and to give you a meal every night. This is a huge help since your bank account has been hovering in the low hundreds for a couple of months now. Of course, you are still paying rent and bills for your apartment hundreds of miles away—the place you haven't seen in months.

You tiptoe around the unfamiliar house, not wanting to wake these near strangers. Finding a cereal bowl and the milk takes longer than you thought it would, but seven minutes later you're out the door and plugging the address of the hospital into the GPS. The GPS estimates the drive to be twenty-five minutes, longer than you'd like but doable for a month. No music in the car this morning—you want to be able to hear the GPS directions. Nothing is worse than showing up late the first day. Thankfully the hospital is easy to spot from the road—a looming rectangle with a name in bright red lit up against the dark sky. First-day jitters caused your foot to be heavier than normal, and you reach the hospital in twenty minutes. The one-page detailed account the administrator sent you of how and where to park is confusing—there are two parking structures—and your anxiety rises. You pull into the one that seems closer to the hospital, the one for visitors, the one that you will never be able to park in again.

Every hospital lobby seems to have the same strange artwork, banners telling you it is the best around, perhaps a framed picture of the illustrious family that funded the west wing. Clad in your white coat and professional attire, you make your way toward the front desk. The security guard instantly notices your look of confusion and prepares himself for a question he's been asked a million times.

"Hi, I'm a rotating student, and this is my first day at this hospital—"

He interrupts. "You looking for the education administration office?"

"Yeah."

"Walk straight down that hallway. Take your first right. There will be an elevator on your left. Take it to the fourth floor, and then take an immediate left."

Concentrating too hard on the first part of the directions causes you to miss the last part, but you depart in a hurry, calling, "Okay, thanks," and you manage to get lost at least three times before finally reaching the education administration office.

Unfortunately, all the lights are off and a quick twist of the unyielding doorknob reveals that the door is locked. Well, it's only 6:52. They aren't supposed to be here for at least eight minutes. Fifteen minutes later, a short, portly woman in her mid-fifties with a short bob haircut opens the door. She looks exactly as you'd imagined her the first time you saw her e-mail correspondence written in all caps. She asks what school you hail from, and you engage in a friendly conversation about places in the area. After ten minutes of chatting and paper shuffling, she hands you your itinerary for the day.

Once again you are about to begin the proverbial first day scavenger hunt, a familiar event in an unfamiliar place. The first item to find is the ID badge; this is followed by a parking tag, scrub access, and the ever-feared last item, always the same: the resident room—throw yourself in and see what happens. With a long sigh, you say goodbye to the friendly administrator and start your journey. Getting the ID badge is easy enough, although you never know whether or not to smile so your photo always ends up with a weird half smile. By now you have enough ID badges from all your previous rotations to start a collection. After a few hours of walking and waiting, you stand proudly with your ID badge clipped on, scrub access obtained, and parking tag purchased. Before taking the dreaded last step you decide to treat yourself to a nice breakfast. This isn't your first rodeo, and you know the residents don't know what time you're supposed to get there. Sometimes they don't even know you're coming at all. What's more, you never know when your next meal will be, so breakfast is an insurance policy against hunger.

After an efficient fifteen-minute meal and a quick bathroom stop, you are ready to head up to the resident room. Ten minutes and three wrong turns later, you're staring at a door with the words *Resident Room* plastered on it. You take a deep breath and knock timidly. Twenty seconds pass and you start to wonder whether you should knock again. Just as you raise your fist, the door swings open and you are staring into the puzzled face of a resident. Your fist swings down into handshake formation as you make eye contact and introduce yourself: "Hi, I'm Alex from Northern State medical school and I'm rotating here this month."

"Hey, nice to meet you. I'm George," he answers. He shakes your hand and turns, and you instinctively follow him into the resident room, like a dog that has waited all day to greet his master. The first thing you notice is that this room, like every other resident room, does not have nearly enough space for the number of people and things it must contain. In the center stands a sizeable table surrounded by innumerable chairs. A large bookshelf takes up the back wall, though the books look as if they haven't been moved for fifteen years. A few desktop computers sit toward the back of the room. Papers are everywhere. Eight residents, some in scrubs, some in office attire, some well groomed, and some not, are occupied either talking on the phone or doing paperwork. Meeting a large group of people at once is always awkward, and it's even more awkward when none of them are paying any attention to you. Unsure about what to do, you stand in the entrance until eventually one of the residents glances up, and you step forward to introduce yourself. While half the residents seem to ignore your existence, the other half stop what they are doing and give you a quick name and a handshake. Now if only you could remember their names. After the quick introductions, the residents return to their tasks and you continue standing there, feeling like an idiot. Thankfully, one of the residents looks up at you again and says, "Here is a list of the surgeries going on today. You could go into one of these two rooms, but first talk to the other med student."

Suddenly, a resident you haven't met yet says, "Follow me. I'll show you where to go." He motions with one hand for you to follow him out the doors he's opening with his other hand. Right outside the room he says, "I don't think we met. My name is Tyler and I'm a med student from Southern State medical school."

"Oh...I didn't realize...I thought you were a resident," you stammer.

"I wish. But no, I'm in the same boat as you. This is my second week here. I was planning to go into room 13, so would you be cool with room 14?"

It's then you realize that room 14 isn't set to go until 3:00 p.m., when the attending finishes his clinic, while room 13 is set to start in the next hour. What's more is that the attending in room 13 is the chair of the program—the person who has the most say in choosing next year's resident class. Of course Tyler would pick room 13 over room 14. Who wouldn't? Tyler tells you how he really wants to work with the program chair and that he has essentially staked out room 13 for days. So be it, you think. He gives you the whole rundown of which residents are the cool ones, which attendings he has worked with, and how scary each is. You hesitate before asking the ever-important question, the answer to which will set the tone for the next month.

"So what time do you get here in the morning?" *Please don't be insanely early, please don't be insanely early.*

Tyler smirks and answers, "Well, I usually try to get here around 4:30. Sometimes I get in a little later; it depends on the day."

"Crap!" You say out loud, and your shock is visible on your face. Tyler seems to be feeding off your anxiety. You don't even bother asking him what time he gets out because you don't want to know. He shows you where the lockers, scrub machine, and OR are, and you figure you'll change and walk back up to the resident room to see if anyone needs help with anything before the surgery starts.

Unfortunately, this time only two residents are in the resident room, neither of whom needs help. It almost seems as if no one cares where you go, but since you want to impress, you walk back down to the OR area to see if anyone there needs help with anything. Fifteen minutes and five wrong turns later, you find yourself in preop, where you spot Tyler on the heels of one of the chief residents. Well, it's good that he at least knows what he's doing today, you think sarcastically.

Roaming around preop, you find a couple of residents doing paperwork, but you're not sure if either is one of your residents. You throw an awkward glance at an ID badge for confirmation. Yes, that is the right resident. The person behind the badge glances up, and you jump to introduce yourself. As it turns out, he's waiting to go into the same surgery you are. After some conversation, you learn he grew up near your hometown, and little by little you discover you have a great deal in common. He's easy to talk to, and the next two hours pass quickly as you follow him around while he does paperwork. Even though you're useless to him, talking to someone friendly feels good.

At 3:00 p.m., there's no sign of the attending. *He must be having a late clinic day*, you think as 3:00 turns to 4:00 turns to 5:00 and then 6:00 p.m. and you've spent the day wandering through the hospital. Although you prefer this to a day spent doing menial paperwork as has happened in past rotations, it still sucks. At 6:03 p.m., the resident gets word that the attending has just entered the building. The resident is nice enough to introduce you to the attending, who gives you a quick hello. He clearly wants to get out of the hospital as badly as you do. Thankfully, the day gains some momentum and by 6:10, you are scrubbing in. The scrub tech gives you an evil eye as she asks you if you have scrubbed in before. You give her a confident yes, followed by your inner and outer glove sizes. Apparently, this is enough to placate her as she asks the OR nurse for your gloves and an extra gown. Fortunately, this surgery isn't supposed to take all night. Your best guess is an hour and a half. It's 8:05 when you and the resident finally leave the room. As he sits down he says, "I'm just going to do some paperwork; you should get out of here." Some med students might take this as a sign to stay all night. You, on the other hand, are saner.

"Are you sure you don't need help with anything?" you ask.

"No. Seriously, you should go home."

You nod and tell him okay. As you are leaving you remember to ask, "Hey, what time do we start in the morning?"

"Usually we start at 5:45, so be here then."

"Will do. See you then," you say with a big smile. You start to wonder how crazy Tyler actually is.

You notice that it's just as dark outside as when you arrived, but the ride back to your girlfriend's mother's friend's house is quick. Your housemates are curious to hear about your first day, and you tell them, "It was a typical first day." About an hour and a half later you are snuggled in bed—with two alarms set. You sigh deeply as you sink into sleep and try not to think too much about the trials and tribulations of tomorrow.

Pros and Cons of Away Rotations

The away rotation is a unique experience for most medical students as it gives them an opportunity to see how another institution functions. Away rotations usually last a month and can be done in any specialty, from psychiatry to plastic surgery. Normally you'll do them in the earlier part of the fourth year at a place you're considering going for your residency. Some medical students might do up to three away rotations (even more if they are particularly intense students), while some won't do any. The more competitive a specialty is, the more necessary an away rotation becomes because while it allows a student to get to know a residency program, it also allows a residency program to get to know the student. Most programs will grant interviews to all the students who have rotated through. Considering how hard it is to get interviews in some specialties, away rotations can mean the difference between being matched and not being matched.

You need to consider many pros and cons in deciding whether or not to do an away rotation. The biggest pro, besides getting an almost guaranteed interview, is that the away rotation allows you to get a good feel for a specific program. Interview day gives but a glimpse of a program, and that is often a biased glimpse presented by the faculty and residents who want to make the program seem desirable. If you rotate in a program, you'll know how it functions day to day, knowledge far more helpful than anything a resident or faculty member says about the program. You might choose to rotate at a place you've always wanted to go for residency but change your mind after a couple of days rotating there. Without doing an away rotation, you might have ended up at a place where ultimately you would have been unhappy. Conversely, you might pick an away rotation out of convenience only to fall in love with the program and make it your number one choice. Even if you decide you don't want to go to that institution for residency, the experience may help you discover what kind of place you do want to attend. Away rotations at different types of institutions can give you a great idea of what type of institution would make you most happy. If you never do an away rotation, you could falsely assume that the way your home institution operates is the way every institution operates.

Another big pro of doing an away rotation is that some institutions tend to rank their rotators higher than they do nonrotators. Residency programs expend as much effort trying to find the right residents as students expend trying to find the right residency program. They invest time, money, and other resources into educating doctors, and the decision about which residents to choose will be one the program lives with for years. If a resident fits in well with the program, everyone is happy. If a resident ends up being a problem, he or she will be a burden the program has to bear for a long time. That is why residency interviews exist—as one more step in the data-gathering process, an opportunity for the program to better assess if the interviewee would be a good fit for the program. Of course, anyone can fool someone for the length of an interview, and residency programs know this and know they are taking a chance on someone they have talked to for only a few hours. A rotating student is much less of a risk as a result. Fooling someone for a whole month is hard. Indeed, some programs in competitive specialties unofficially require students to complete an away rotation before they will offer even an interview.

The cons of the away rotation can include the costs and logistics. While the rotation itself is generally free, room and board most often aren't. On top of the rent and bills you're already paying for housing near your home institution, the extra costs can be prohibitive. The matter is made worse if you must rent a car or rely on public transportation. An easy solution is to stay with family, friends, long-lost relatives, or anyone you have any inkling you might be connected to. Even if friends and family live farther away from the hospital then you might like, the few extra minutes of the commute are probably worth the huge savings if they're offering a free or reduced-rate room. In fact, a fair number of students choose their away rotations based on where they can stay for free. Also, you'll want to strongly consider bringing your car to an away rotation, even if you live twenty hours away. Except in some of the biggest cities, having a car is a huge convenience.

Away rotations can be a pain when it comes to scheduling. Although the average fourth-year schedule is relatively flexible to allow time for electives, interviewing, and studying for the Step 2s, properly scheduling electives and free time can still be a challenge. You may have to take a required elective at a time when you wanted to do an away rotation, and if you're last in line choosing your fourth-year schedule, this becomes a particularly troubling issue. The later in line you are, the harder it becomes to fit in everything. This issue can be further complicated if the block schedule of your home institution does not align with the block schedule of the away institution. When institutions' schedules are staggered, you'll usually lose a week between the end of one rotation and the start of another, though the upside is that this week can be a nice rest period or may give you ample time to travel to your next rotation.

Away rotations can be mentally draining, particularly if you're doing multiple rotations back to back. An away rotation is reminiscent of a long interview. Almost every day you'll have new attendings to meet and opportunities to work with residents with whom you haven't worked—especially at large institutions with many residents—which means you'll have to continually work to make good first impressions. Sometimes, you'll have just one chance to work with a certain attending or resident, and the first impression you make will end up being the only impression. If you mess something up, the attending or resident might remember only that about you. Since you never really know how much input a specific attending or resident has in the match rankings, one mistake could be disastrous. This puts much mental strain on you to be at your best during every moment of every day, and being in an unfamiliar setting only contributes to the difficulty. Not knowing your way around or where anything is can be stressful anyway, and often you'll have no friends in the area, which can make time outside the hospital lonely. On the other hand, your time outside the hospital that isn't used for sleeping might be minimal, and if you're staying with family or have many friends in the area, you could have a great time in your (minimal) off hours.

Away rotations can also be physically draining. The desire to do well usually translates into showing up early, staying late, and volunteering to do everything. Showing up in the morning after all the residents have arrived or leaving the hospital in the afternoon (or evening) before all the residents leave will leave the impression that you are not committed and that you're lazy. When asked by a resident to do or see something, motivated students will almost always say yes.

"Hey, do you want to see a cool case that is set to go at 8:00 tonight?"
"Yeah. Definitely."
"Hey, do you mind finding me the patient's chart?"
"No problem."
"When are you taking call next?"
"Um, Thursday."

The hours you put in on an away rotation may be the most hours you have ever worked in four weeks, but not every away rotation is necessarily harder than your home rotation. Regardless, trying to impress everyone all the time will take its toll.

Deciding Whether to Do an Away Rotation

As I said, anyone considering going into a supercompetitive specialty should do away rotations, but what about those who aren't? They don't need to do away rotations, but that doesn't mean doing one is entirely superfluous. Although the probability of being matched to a noncompetitive specialty is high for most medical students, many competitive, desirable programs in that specialty are hard to be matched to. Doing an away rotation at a competitive program will help you get your foot in the door of a program you otherwise would not have had a chance of being matched to. In other words, for less-competitive specialties, doing an away rotation at a "reach" program makes sense. Another good reason to do an away rotation in a less-competitive field is to see how another institution functions. This will provide invaluable information on the type of place that might make you happiest. Last, some students decide to do an away rotation in an area they want to visit for a month. But while living at home with Mom and Dad for a while may be nice, remember that away rotations are often strenuous and you may not have much time available outside the hospital for other activities you plan.

The decision about whether or not to do an away rotation in a non-competitive specialty is up to the student. Each individual must weigh the pluses and minuses to make the best decision. Those with children find it especially tough to justify leaving home and paying double rent for a month. Sometimes, the away rotation just won't fit properly into a schedule. On the other hand, those who are dead set on a specific competitive program will probably benefit from doing an away rotation there.

Choosing Away Rotations

Once you decide to do an away rotation, you'll have to figure out when, how many, and where. The rotator season usually is between the end of the third year and the start of interview season, usually meaning the months of July through November, although some students are able to arrange away rotations during their third-year elective time. Also, interview seasons are not the same for all specialties—some are on the early side and may be finished by the middle of December, while others will push toward the end of January.

You'll want to consider the pluses and minuses of scheduling away rotations. Doing them too early will mean that months will go by before interviews are conducted and the residency program may forget about the first students who rotated there. This may be especially true if a program has a lot of rotators. Regardless, if you do a stellar job on your rotation, people will remember you despite the passage of time. Doing an away rotation toward the end of rotation season doesn't present too many issues, but you'll want to be careful not to push it into interview season, as this will surely cause you to miss many days of a rotation. One good approach is to ask one of the residents in your desired specialty what months he went on interviews, and then keep those months as free as possible.

The truth is, most students don't have much of a choice when it comes to deciding what months to do away rotations. Usually after you sign up for your required fourth-year rotations, only a small period of time will be left for electives and away rotations—and with luck this will be during rotation season. Everything depends on how early you are able to pick your rotations in the fourth-year lottery. Most students do away rotations when it fits with their schedule, but if a student has some flexibility in her schedule, the question becomes whether she ought to do her specialty-specific home rotations or away rotations first. There are many pros and cons to consider when scheduling away rotations before or after your home rotations (see chapter 10, "The Fourth Year in a Nutshell"). Suffice it to say for now that doing home rotations first will provide ample time to get letters of recommendation and will provide a crash course in an unfamiliar specialty, but doing your home rotations first might not allow you enough time to get letters of recommendation from attendings at an away rotation.

The next question is, How many away rotations should you do? As discussed earlier, for those in a noncompetitive specialty, doing one away rotation at a desired institution may make sense, while those in competitive fields usually wind up doing two to three away rotations. Some students do even more, but be cautioned about doing too many. Most medical schools will give only so much credit for away rotations. (At most schools, they are considered elective time.) Each school is different, so you'll want to find out the specifics of elective time before scheduling anything. Be aware that doing many months of away rotations could result in less free time to interview and could even cause you to graduate late! (No one wants to graduate weeks after everyone else.) Having less free time to interview will no doubt increase travel costs as you'll have to travel back and forth from your home rotation to your interviews. Also remember that away rotations are draining, and doing too many may lead to burnout.

You may want to do a number of away rotations but not have enough elective time. A great solution to this problem is to ask the institutions where you're considering rotating if a three- or two-week rotation is possible instead of the standard four-week rotation. Most institutions have no problem allowing this as they are aware that students' fourth-year schedules are complicated and potentially unyielding. They would rather have a student rotate for fewer than four weeks than not rotate at all. Also, three weeks is plenty of time for you to get to know the program and for the program to get to know you. A two-week rotation might be somewhat short, especially at a large institution, but in a smaller program, you will have enough time to get to know everyone, and two weeks will certainly allow enough time for you to form an opinion of the program. In the end, a two-week trade-off for an extra interview is not a bad deal.

The next and perhaps the hardest question to answer about away rotations is, Where should you do them? Some students have had a dream institution since the day they were born. Still, most students have a tough time picking two or three institutions given the number of unknowns to consider. Often students choose to rotate at a residency program without knowing anything about it except the name. A rotator I once met told me that the month he spent at a big-name institution was the worst month of his entire life. He ended up hating the program so much, he didn't even apply there for residency! Nothing is worse than spending a month stuck in a rotation at a program you don't want to attend. On the other hand, some students end up loving places they never imagined they would.

Information about specific programs is hard to come by, and reading an institution's website won't prove much use. Remember, the main advantage of an away rotation is that it usually grants the rotator an interview, thus placing the rotator a step above the nonrotating interviewees. Some institutions, however, will have five to ten times the number of rotators as available first-year resident positions and thus may not grant an interview to all rotators. Even if they do, the competition for those few spots will be fierce, and what ordinarily is an advantage is diminished in importance. Be cautious about doing a rotation at a place like this unless it is your dream program. Also, some programs end up being matched with mostly nonrotators. This could be because of the program's preference or because most rotators hated the time they spent rotating there. Either way, if an institution doesn't have a majority of residency positions filled by people who rotated there (this includes students from the program's home institution), consider that a bad sign.

It's hard to know which places have an abundance of rotators, don't interview all their rotators, or don't get matched with many rotators. The best way to find this information is to contact the program coordinator, whom you might think of as the secretarial glue that holds a residency program together. Program coordinators are basically in charge of coordinating almost everything and keeping residency programs running like well-oiled machines. They are the go-to people for questions about their residency programs, and their contact information usually is accessible through a program's web page. Definitely ask a program coordinator how many rotators the program generally has, how many of those rotators get interviews, and how many rotators plus home students it ends up being matched with. If a program has few rotators, it grants interviews to all rotators, and most of the students who are matched there were rotators, it's likely a good place to rotate. If you are unable to contact the program coordinator, finding the answers to the above questions may be difficult. Contacting the residents themselves with questions about rotating isn't the best idea because they probably don't know all the answers and are so busy they will probably never respond anyway. A program's website usually has some information about the residents that are currently in the program, so you can at least know which schools a residency program usually takes students from. If all else fails, try using a message board, though take any information from a message board with a giant grain of salt as you won't be able to tell what the source of the information really is.

Another important factor is whether an institution where you're considering rotating is thought of as a "malignant" program—a place where the residents are overworked, underappreciated, and generally unhappy. Chances are, if every single resident is unhappy, you would be too. Finding out if a program is malignant can be challenging without experiencing it firsthand, but it may be worth asking the residents at your home institution if they have heard anything about a specific program. Most of the time residents won't be familiar with the program and thus will have no opinion, but if a majority say they heard the program is miserable, it is probably a malignant program.

In the end, you'll decide for yourself where you would like to rotate, and once you decide, you can apply to most programs through an online application service called the Visiting Student Application Service (VSAS). Almost every program will have a page on the VSAS website that states its application requirements and the opening date. Most applications require immunization records and a curriculum vitae, although some will require tests scores, a photo, or even an essay. The cost is based on how many institutions a student applies to, which usually amounts to less than $100, and applying through VSAS is easy (although gathering every immunization record since birth can be a pain). When you apply, you'll get to pick the time period during which you'd like to do a rotation. And as with any application process, you need to submit your application as soon as possible.

One common question from students is, How many schools should I apply to through VSAS? Most people get what they request. However, rotations at certain institutions are harder to get. This might be because the time period requested is filled by the home institution's students, who have priority, or there might simply not be enough spots. One approach is to apply to a lot of away rotations, though if you are accepted to many, you'll have to turn some down, and the rejected institutions may not look favorably upon your decision. It is hard to know whether this will affect your chances for obtaining an interview later on. Some students apply only to the programs they want to attend, and if they are rejected for a rotation, they apply to another program. This can be risky though because by the time you have heard about your status, spots at other institutions may be filled. However, if all spots aren't filled, this strategy works fine.

It's a good idea to contact the program coordinator of a program in question to ask how competitive the program is for a given time period. If you find out that it is highly competitive, applying to another "safety" institution isn't a bad idea. If the program administrator says that most people end up getting their requested time period, applying to a safety institution is probably not necessary.

VSAS is not the only avenue through which to obtain an away rotation. Some programs, in fact, do not participate in VSAS. A lot of under-the-radar institutions have very good programs that most students don't know about simply because the schools don't have big names. And since they aren't on VSAS, they normally don't get as many requests for away rotations as do the institutions that are on VSAS. Applying to these programs can dramatically increase the statistical advantage that you'll gain from doing a rotation there. Also, securing an away rotation spot at these institutions is relatively easy, requiring only an e-mail or phone call to the coordinator. Oftentimes these programs are flexible regarding the time period as well. Some of these lesser-known programs are truly diamonds in the rough.

Doing Well in an Away Rotation

After applying and (hopefully) being accepted and arranging a future living situation, the final step is to actually do the away rotation. Doing well on an away rotation is similar to doing well on any standard rotation with a few caveats. Most institutions offer away rotations only to students they will consider interviewing. Therefore, almost all students who rotate have the credentials to obtain a residency position (apart from some supercompetitive programs that don't interview all their rotators). Most residency programs don't want to waste their time on students whom they never planned to accept. And as discussed earlier, a rotator generally has an advantage over a nonrotator. However, this assumes that the rotator does a good job. If he does a bad job, he'll actually be at a disadvantage.

How do you do well on an away rotation? The goal of away rotations for residency programs is to help them find the students they want as residents for the upcoming year. This translates to the students they think would be the best fit in their programs. The term *fit* is nebulous at best, but residency programs want to find students who have good credentials, work hard, and function harmoniously within the machinery of the program. Credentials don't matter on an away rotation for two reasons. The first is that all the rotators have fairly good credentials as determined by the residency program; they wouldn't be able to rotate there if they didn't. This creates a level playing field of sorts. The second is that if a student is difficult to work with, the program won't care about publications or board scores—that student will end up being an undesirable residency candidate.

Working hard is always part of doing well on any rotation. The program wants to know if you can handle resident-like hours while doing a good job. This means showing up early, staying until the work is done, and helping out as much as possible. On time is usually considered late. Showing up after all the residents have arrived sends the wrong message. But you don't have to show up hours before the residents do. The advantage of being the first one in the room is that those who arrive after you don't know how long you've been there. For example, if you arrive five minutes before the first resident does, the resident might assume you've been there for half an hour. However, just being at the hospital for a lot of hours won't do you any good if you just stand there. Try to assist the residents and attendings as much as possible, taking the initiative to help in any way you can without being asked. Be willing to help with even the most menial tasks.

There is one caveat. If you work too hard, you might be perceived as annoying or too intense. So stick around and help out until all the work is finished. But if there's nothing for you to do and the resident in charge tells you to go home, go home. Otherwise, the resident might wonder why you don't value your own time. On the flip side, more intense residency programs respect students who simply do not leave. That said, most residents aren't trying to test the rotators; they're looking out for them. Another helpful tip is to ask the residents which attendings have the most influence in ranking students for the match. Residents will almost always be able to tell you who among the attendings is more important to work with, and once you know, try to work with these attendings as much as possible without ignoring others or being unfair to your fellow rotators.

One positive note is that working hard on an away rotation is generally easier than working hard on any other rotation for three reasons. First, you'll likely be more motivated because you're rotating in your desired specialty. Second, you're usually away from your friends and living in a foreign environment, which means you have less to go home to, and this makes staying at the hospital for an extra few hours less repugnant. Third, you normally won't have any assignments to complete or tests to study for on an away rotation, which makes spending more time at the hospital easier. Be cautioned that some away rotations require a presentation—one usually given to the program director or chair at the end of the rotation. As a rotating student you might not know you have to give a presentation until halfway through the rotation because no one bothered to tell you. This creates a stressful situation, but you can avoid this calamity by either looking at the syllabus of the rotation beforehand or asking the residents if any assignments are due.

The concept of working hard is easy to fathom: put in a lot of hours and effort. Figuring out how to function harmoniously within the machinery of the residency program is a little harder. It is more or less equivalent to your making everybody associated with the residency program like you. No doubt on some third-year rotations, two students who work equally hard will receive far different grades. This unfairness stems from the fact that whoever is in charge of giving evaluations happens to like one student more than the other, and the reason for this could be anything from degree of clinical skills to which football team the favored student roots for. The situation is similar in an away rotation, except that here you are trying to secure a residency position rather than a good evaluation. All other things being equal (credentials, work ethic, time put in, attitude), residency programs want to find someone that they wouldn't mind having around for the next few years. In other words, they want to find students that they like.

How do you make a whole residency program like you? There is no secret answer to this question. Some people just get along well with others, and some don't. We all have people we call friends and other people who aren't friends. It's hard to explain the why of this. Even so you can take steps to avoid having those associated with the residency program dislike you.

First, respect everybody in the hospital. Respecting the attendings is a given as they ultimately choose the next incoming class. Respecting the residents is equally important. In some institutions, the residents have almost as much say as the attendings in creating the rank list. If a majority of the residents don't like you, you'll be unlikely to be matched there, even if the attendings love you. This applies not only to the chief residents but to all the residents. Most of the residents in a specialty are friendly with each other, and if you get along poorly with a certain resident, that resident likely will not speak kindly of you to the others. Before you know it, you'll have a sour reputation. It's also important to be respectful and nice to ancillary staff. While they seldom have a say in choosing the incoming class of residents, they can influence how a resident or attending feels about you. A lot of attendings and residents become friends with the ancillary staff through years of working together. If you offend a nurse, that nurse could easily tell an attending or resident about your bad behavior, and this could hurt your chances of being matched there.

Second, always dress appropriately and be well groomed. You'll make first impressions almost every day, and looking sloppy will reflect poorly on you. The extra effort required to dress in clean clothes, to shave, and to style your hair is definitely worth it.

Third, act professionally in your daily interactions with patients. Making inappropriate gestures and saying inappropriate comments will make you look terrible. Sometimes the residents will joke with each other, and sometimes those jokes won't be politically correct. Humor, of course, is a great way to diffuse stressful situations, and you'll want to laugh along with the residents, but be cautious about what you say so as not to offend anyone. You may not know the residents as well as you think you do, and you could easily cause offense. If you think something is truly funny and won't offend anyone, say it—but always use your common sense.

While it is hard to define exactly what a given program is looking for, four common personality traits are highly undesirable. These are being a complainer, being annoying, behaving weirdly, and above all, being lazy. Unfortunately, those who are weird or annoying usually don't realize they are. Some people naturally make inappropriate or strange comments or have a tendency to bother everyone. These are the students who wind up ruining their chances at an institution by doing an away rotation. In fact, such students should be encouraged not to do an away rotation because it will probably only hurt them. Those who are only somewhat weird or annoying need to curb their personality quirks while on an away rotation by thinking about everything before saying it. In other words, they must avoid yielding to the tendency to blurt.

Controlling a tendency to complain is much easier than is controlling a tendency to be weird or be annoying. For some people, complaining is natural and no doubt influenced by the difficulty of an away rotation. Complaining about the hours, tough call nights, and the general unfairness of life can feel good, and being stuck doing menial tasks that provide no learning opportunities naturally generates opportunities for complaint. But remember, no one wants to hear a student complain, especially not the residents. They're likely working harder and putting in more hours than the rotators are, and complaining to them will win you no points.

Being lazy is the ultimate sin for a rotator, as a lazy rotator will no doubt make a lazy resident someday. And since residents are already overworked, the last problem they would want to have is picking up the slack that a lazy resident left behind. There is no quicker way to ruin your chances of being matched at a given institution than to be perceived as lazy.

Summary

While away rotations can be tough and inconvenient, doing them is a fascinating experience that can provide a huge advantage for fourth-year medical students by helping them match at a specific institution and giving them insight into how different programs function. For ultracompetitive specialties, doing multiple away rotations could mean the difference between being matched and remaining unmatched.

Choosing your away rotations can be difficult. Ultimately you'll need to see what is possible considering the constraints of your existing fourth-year schedule. Remember, some institutions are flexible with their rotation dates, and they may be able to work with you. Also, program coordinators are your best source of knowledge and can help you determine whether doing an away rotation at their institution will provide you with a real advantage. Finally, try your best to work hard, take initiative, and act professional, while avoiding being a complainer, acting annoying, being lazy, or behaving weirdly.

Keep in mind that while residencies are trying to find the students who are the best fit for their programs, rotators should also be trying to find the program that is the best fit for them. And as with any rotation, you can only do your best and hope that everything works out.

12 | The Residency Interview

The sun set a long time ago, and the air is crisp. Your shivering causes your pace to quicken as you move toward your frosty car, which is parked a quarter mile away. A sigh leaves your lips as the thought enters your brain that you may have consumed too much this evening. It's hard to avoid stuffing yourself when everything is free. Those couple of beers didn't help either. This is your sixth preinterview dinner, and you're growing tired of them. Even though the atmosphere at these events is relaxed, walking into a room of residents whom you don't know and forcing yourself to be social is always anxiety provoking and awkward. Fortunately, you are starting to recognize some of the other applicants as the interview season carries on, as some of them seem to be on the exact same interview schedule as you are. You might even call some of them friends. Most of the residents are easy to talk to and friendly enough, but you hate the feeling that you should be talking with them as much as possible and constantly asking questions. Of course, you know that the preinterview dinner provides a great chance to get to know the residents and to get a feel for the program, but all you want to do is eat free food and talk with the other applicants. That way you don't have to mind your every word and gesture. *Well, thankfully that's done*, you think while plugging the coordinates of your hotel into the GPS.

It's clearly excessive to set your cell phone alarm, set the hotel clock alarm, and ask for a wake-up call, but you didn't drive all the way out here to miss this interview. The extra alarms will pacify your irrational fear of sleeping late. *This interview process is starting to add up*, you think while trying to fight the urge to calculate the total cost. Luckily, you're paying half price for the hotel room. The "discount" hotel rooms that programs normally offer are much more expensive than the rates available on the name-your-own-price website. That was easily the best interview tip you received.

The cacophony of three alarms is deafening and confusing, but the desired effect is achieved. You're on your feet, stepping over all the pillows you tossed off the bed last night. It's 5:45 a.m., and the interview check-in isn't until 7:30. This should give you more than enough time to get fresh, clean, and sharp looking. Also, you have to pack up your belongings, as after today's interview you need to drive five hours west toward tomorrow's interview. The thought that you won't be able to make the next preinterview dinner is pleasing.

The nice part about leaving so early in the morning is that there is hardly any traffic. After fifteen minutes of easy driving, the hospital comes into view. It looks different from the picture of it on the website. That picture must have been taken twenty years ago. The three-paragraph account of parking specifics the program coordinator sent out is disheartening. *If worse comes to worst I can park in the visitors' section*, you think. You have an out-of-state license plate and you'll be there just one day.

The heat of the hospital feels good on your cold face. You still feel, somewhat stubbornly, that leaving your coat in the car was a good idea. Who wants to carry that thing around all day? Clad in your new suit and fancy shoes, you proceed toward the security guard, who knows instantly where you are going. "Go back over there and follow the signs that say 'interview,'" he says. You nod and follow his directions. The last arrow is vertical rather than horizontal, and you realize that you are standing outside the "interview lobby." A quick peek inside reveals a handful of people, all wearing the same suit as you.

Most of the applicants in the room are either chatting or looking at the packet of information they were given. The friendly smile of the woman at the front desk catches your eye, and she jumps at the chance to say hello. Her voice is high pitched and excited as she explains that she is the program coordinator. *So that's what the program administrator looks like.* It catches you off guard as you always pictured her differently. "Please sign the form, find your nametag, and grab a packet, and then you can have a seat over there," she says while motioning to the array of available gray plush seats to her left. You chuckle at the thought of not signing the form—that's completely insane. One minute and four scribbles later, you hand in the form and grab a brightly colored packet with your name on it. You reflect that the packet is a little heavier than you thought it would be. A quick glance around the room reveals a familiar face, which puts you at ease. You haven't seen this student for three days, but you're on similar interview schedules, and the conversation between you is easy. You both talk about where you've been, travel inconveniences, and where you are headed to next. After a few minutes, the conversation turns to non-medical-related topics.

After twenty minutes of pleasant conversation, you open the heavy packet. Every packet contains only one important piece of paper: the interview schedule. The rest is just information on how great the hospital and residency program are along with information about resident benefits and such. You're familiar with that information since you read it online last night. Your day consists of four fifteen-minute interviews with pairs of faculty, all of which are before noon. You hate interviewing after lunch as the increased blood flow to your stomach takes away some of the blood flow to your brain. Another glance at the interview schedule reveals that your applicant buddy is set to go after lunch.

"Awww, man, I'm the last interview of the day!" he says glumly.

"I feel for you; we've all been there. Just don't eat too much at lunch."

"Looks like you're at the beginning of the day," he says.

"Yeah, guess I was just lucky this time. I do have to drive five hours after this."

"Oh, I've only got to drive two."

It's 7:45 and every applicant has arrived. At 8:30 the program coordinator walks back in the room and says, "Everyone, please follow me for the chair's presentation." And like clockwork, a herd of suits amasses behind her. After a few minutes of lefts and rights, she leads you into a large room with a projector and dozens of seats. Everyone files in neatly, and a minute later the department chair appears. He looks exactly like his picture on the website. These presentations are all the same. You hear about the size of the hospital, the block schedule of the various rotations, and accolades for residents' research and other kudos. He ends by showing you pictures of the residents doing fun activities outside the hospital. Five minutes after he finishes, you find yourself back in the interview lobby with the other applicants.

The following hour passes quickly as the conversation you're having with your friend is engaging. Time slows dramatically when your applicant buddy leaves on the hospital tour. One moment after another drags on as several of the residents pass in and out of the room, answering questions. The downtime causes you to reflect on the program. The residents here seem happy, and the program generally fits with what you are looking for. Of course, you aren't so fond of a few aspects, but you like most of the program. You may end up ranking it higher than you originally thought you would. Just then, a woman you've never seen peeks her head into the room. She's holding a piece of paper and begins to call out names. Yours is one of them. You quickly rise, put down your packet, button your suit jacket, and make your way over toward her.

"You will interview first with Dr. Houston and Dr. Barnaby. Follow me," she says curtly.

A few brief moments later, you find yourself in front of a heavy wooden door in a long hallway. She knocks, opens the door a foot, and waits for a reply.

"Yup, we're ready; send him in," one of the doctors says. You sigh as you open the door wide, step in, and try to make eye contact with both doctors at the same time. They stand just enough to shake your hand and introduce themselves. "Please have a seat," one says.

Both doctors flip through a packet that is no doubt your ERAS application. You start to wonder how much of it they have read beforehand. It's hard to know what to expect. Most of the interview questions you've had to answer thus far have been pretty normal: Why do you want to go into this specialty? Tell me about your research. What sets you apart from all the other candidates? Some have been a little oddball: What is your stance on gun control? If you could have dinner with anyone alive or dead, who would it be and why? What would you do if you couldn't do this specialty? And then some have been downright strange: Why don't you want to be a ballerina? What's your second favorite band? What animal would you want to be and why? What's your best Halloween costume? Also, one aspect of your application gets brought up at every interview.

"So tell me about this pizza website business," one of the doctors says as she glances up from your packet. The year before medical school, you and a couple of friends tried to find the best pizza in your hometown, and you thought you might as well document the journey on a website. The site became more popular than you ever thought it would, and four years later it is still up and running with new posts every month or two. You thought this might be an interesting item to list in the "hobbies" section of your ERAS application. Little did you know that on the interview trail you would be discussing the pizza website more than any other topic. You begin to go into the details of the pizza rating algorithm and explain the pizza tournament you once held. The smiles on the doctors' faces grow as they realize how much pizza you consumed that year.

The rest of the interview passes casually as the interviewing doctors ask you questions you've answered many times before. *So far, so good*, you think. A knock at the door signals that only two minutes are left, and the conversation peters out. The silence creates the opportunity for the question that you're most tired of: "Do you have any questions for us?" It seems that no interviewee can make it through the day without having to answer this question. Unfortunately, last night the residents answered most of your questions. However you know that you will get asked this question in every interview for the rest of the day, so you have a go-to question, an open-ended question you can ask anyone: "What are some advantages of this program as compared to any other program?" In most cases, this question takes up the remaining interview time with ease. This case is no different. Another loud knock signals the end of the interview, and the doctor answering the question abruptly stops what he is saying. You all rise to shake hands and say goodbye, and you fill the last moment by asking them if they want the door open or closed.

The rest of the day's interviews go by without a hitch. Everyone at this program seems relaxed and intent on getting to know you. A glance at your cell phone reveals that it's 11:33. *Not bad*, you think as you reflect on how other interview days have gone on until 4:00. Upon reentering the interview lobby, you are pleased to discover that an incredible lunch spread has somehow materialized. Without hesitation, you fill your plate with everything on the table except the saucy foods that could stain your suit. Thankfully, you are done with the day's interviews; otherwise, there is no way you would eat this much.

After you spend an hour eating and socializing, a resident steps into the interview lobby. "Anyone who hasn't done the tour yet can come with me," he says loudly. About half the suits in the room meander toward him. You sigh—you have overeaten. The tour of this hospital is just like the tour of any other hospital. There's nothing to focus on, so it's more of an after-lunch walk. Casual conversation with another applicant reveals that she was a rotator at this school. You get the lowdown on what it's actually like to work at this hospital. She seems to have liked her rotation here—a good sign. Twenty minutes later, the tour finishes where it started. As you walk back into the interview lobby, you see your buddy sitting with a somewhat sour look on his face. He hasn't done a single interview yet. Telling him that you are all done doesn't help his mood. Well, no reason to stick around here anymore, you think. It's 1:00 p.m., and you have five hours of driving ahead of you. Excited that another interview is done, you make your way to your car, settle into the backseat, and unzip the backpack you prepared the night before. It contains jeans and a T-shirt, comfortable driving clothes. After a few minutes of wriggling in your car, you're changed and ready to go. You hope no one saw you. "Six down, six to go," you say aloud in a weary voice. You will be happy when this is all over.

Residency interviews are probably the last activity of any importance in medical school. Most medical school students have rotations after interviews, but the goal there is usually only to pass as nothing you really do in the second half of the fourth year can affect your future (apart from failing a rotation or getting arrested). Interviewing for a residency can be strenuous, although not as strenuous as a subinternship or hard away rotation. The actual interviews are not difficult; rather, the logistics and strain of traveling around the country in a short period of time can leave you exhausted and stressed.

Planning Ahead

Planning interview trips can be a costly nightmare. Some places offer only a couple of days for interviews, and interview days often overlap between institutions. Often, you'll have to schedule interviews back to back or even cancel some interviews due to time conflicts. Sometimes you'll be lucky enough to have back-to-back interviews in the same area, but more often than not, the interviews will be in different geographical locations. Those students who applied to schools in a wide area will experience this problem more often than those who are looking only in nearby areas. If you're also on a rotation during the time you want to interview, this problem can be compounded. Each rotation allows a student to miss a certain number of days for interviews, so you may be forced into coming back to your home program at inconvenient times, such as between interviews. If your home program is far away from the spots where you're interviewing, the situation is still more expensive and strenuous.

To alleviate the strain and cost of interviewing, you should properly schedule your free time. Most fourth-year schedules are relatively flexible, with a fair amount of free time given for interviewing and taking the Step 2s. Try to schedule as much free time as possible during interview season, allowing you more flexibility with interview planning and avoiding the necessity of flying back and forth to your home institution.

Imagine a student on a home rotation in Georgia who has two interviews in New York City four days apart. Most rotations won't let a student miss five days in a row, so he would have to fly to New York for the first interview, travel back to Georgia for a few days of rotation, and then return to New York for the second interview. This situation is expensive and stressful. Now imagine if he scheduled his free time properly and wasn't on a rotation. He could fly to New York, do two interviews while hanging out for a few days in between—much easier, more enjoyable, and less expensive. Some students will schedule half of their free time at the end of the year so they can graduate early. While this might sound pleasant, it probably won't be worth it if it ends up costing you a lot of extra money in flights and travel expenses.

How do you schedule properly? The first step is to find out when interview season is for the specialty you're interested in. Some specialties may interview in November, while others may interview in January. The best way to find out the duration of an interview season is to ask some of the residents in the desired specialty the range of their interview dates and in what particular period they interviewed most. By doing this, you should be able to get a good idea of when interview season actually is. The next step is to schedule your free time for the most active interview periods. Students who are at the end of the line in the fourth-year rotation-choosing lottery may have to schedule a required elective during interview time. If this happens, try your best to choose a rotation with flexible time periods, such as emergency medicine.

Even if your free time aligns properly with a given interview season, the logistics of doing ten to fifteen interviews can be a nightmare. Ideally, you'll schedule all your interviews in a geographical area during the same time period. Unfortunately, this isn't always possible as some institutions in the same area offer interviews on dates spaced well apart, and some institutions send their interview offers seemingly at random. Sometimes you'll find that two interviews are available in the same city around the same time, but you won't be able to do both because you already have another interview scheduled somewhere else in the same time period. You also might be forced to choose between two institutions that interview on the same day.

You'll be constantly working with an incomplete data set. However, researching every interview date of every institution you apply to won't help much because the combinations are almost endless (especially if you apply to a lot of institutions). There is no easy solution to this problem. Even if your travel arrangements for an interview are inconvenient, it's better than missing the interview altogether. To avoid interview overlap, you might try to schedule interviews on the outskirts of an interview season or choose off dates. For example, an interview on a Sunday in February probably won't overlap with others, while an interview on the first Saturday in January might.

WHAT TO DO WITH PROGRAMS THAT ARE SLOW TO RESPOND

Some residency programs end up never accepting or rejecting a student. I applied to around seventy-five programs and wound up never hearing from about twenty. Why certain programs never send out rejection letters is hard to say. Perhaps they enjoy having a long list of applicants to choose from in case they get a lot of cancellations. It may be worth contacting those programs in question, introducing yourself, and saying, "I'm really interested in your program. I haven't heard back from you yet, but I'm going to be in the area during some of your interview dates." While I didn't try this strategy, I heard it worked for some. Besides, you have little to lose. The worst-case scenario is that you'll be rejected more quickly than you might otherwise have been. At least you'll know where you stand.

When you receive an interview invitation, you'll sometimes have only a few interview dates to choose from. Respond immediately with your preferences, as they are usually offered on a first come, first served basis. It would be a shame to miss an interview because the date you wanted was already filled. It's not a bad idea to accept every interview offer, even if two places interview on the same day. Eventually, you'll have to cancel one of these, but accepting both will provide you ample time to research both institutions and decide which is more desirable.

Keeping track of everything can also be a challenge—especially if you apply to over fifty places. Try your best to stay organized in the chaos that is interview season. Some students create a giant spreadsheet and continually edit it. While this is one approach, computer programs are available that make the process much easier. They aren't free, but having an efficient organizing program with a lot of specifics about many residency programs already filled in is a convenience worth considering.

Once you schedule your interviews, you'll have to make travel arrangements. Obviously, you'll want to take advantage of your connections with anyone who lives in an area close to the program you're visiting. Most people won't mind having a visitor stay for one night. Unfortunately, often you'll have to find a hotel instead. Some residency programs in less-competitive specialties will pay for a hotel, but most programs won't. They will, however, suggest hotels in the area where you can receive a discount by mentioning the residency interview. These are likely to be expensive hotels that are still costly after the discount. You can save more by using a discount name-your-own-price website. Staying for one night even in a less-than-lovely hotel is fine as long as you take care not to stay in a dangerous area. Discount websites can also be used to get lower prices on rental cars, but these sites are trickier for flights since you won't be able to choose your flying time and you may get stuck with layovers. Since you'll likely be working with narrow time margins, your schedule probably won't have that kind of flexibility. It doesn't hurt to look at airports in the general area of one of your programs rather than the nearest. Also, the earlier you book, the less expensive your flight will probably be. Waiting until the last minute will drive the price through the roof. Take care to avoid layovers as bad winter weather and delays could cause you to miss a connecting flight and therefore an interview. You might also want to sign up for an airline miles program at the beginning of interview season; this could provide some convenience later on. Consider driving medium distances or even longer distances if you have multiple interviews in an area at a similar time.

After tackling this logistical nightmare, the focus should shift to the interview itself. Purchase well-fitted, conservative interview attire. The interviewers will judge your every aspect, and unfortunately, appearance is important. Most doctors tend to be on the conservative side, and wearing strange colors could be dangerous.

Read your own application in detail before any interview. The interviewers will almost always have a printout of your ERAS application on their desk, and it is common for them to flip through it and ask questions about specific aspects. If you can't speak intelligently about the topics you have on your own application, you'll look terrible. Some students include research or publications with which they weren't heavily involved on their applications, and while nothing is wrong with this per se, it can become a problem if you aren't able to answer detailed questions about the research.

Knowing your application does not apply just to publications and research but to every single aspect! Some interviewers may spend the whole time discussing what you've listed as your hobbies. Because of my pizza rating website, I spent more time discussing pizza than any other topic on my personal interviews.

Another way to prepare for an interview is to formulate answers to questions that have a high probability of being asked. Always be ready to tell the interviewers about yourself and why you want to go into a specialty or where you see yourself being in ten years. Also, have questions ready to ask the interviewers, because they will no doubt ask for them. Reading about a residency program on the institution's website before an interview is also a good idea. Doing this will help you ask more intelligent questions and show you are truly interested in the program. As the average interview day goes on, you might find you're running out of questions to ask because they have all been answered. If this happens, you can always ask about the advantages or disadvantages of a program or about how efficiently the hospital is run, questions vague enough to elicit lengthy answers that take up the remaining interview time.

Formulating answers to questions that have a lower probability of being asked, such as those described at the start of the chapter, is not a bad idea either. However, preparing for the strangest questions is almost impossible—as when I was asked why I had never wanted to be a ballerina. (I responded that the shoes looked uncomfortable.) Ultimately you'll have to answer some questions on the spot for which you aren't prepared, but you'll become more experienced as the season progresses. Toward the end, the average interviewee will probably have a premeditated response to almost any question. That is, the more interviews you do, the easier they become.

An applicant should also know how to respond to a "stress interview." Most interviews will be laid back, and most interview questions will be reasonable. However, every so often an interviewer will present an applicant with a stress situation that often comes in the form of an oddball question. Sometimes it will be a task to complete (more so for surgical residencies). I once had to pick up a grain of uncooked rice using chopsticks in my nondominant hand and place the rice in a cup. The point was to see how I would respond to stress. Residents responsible for their patients' lives are often exposed to stressful situations, and programs prefer those residents who can stay cool, calm, and collected. The worst thing you can do in such situations is to become flustered and agitated and visibly stressed. Stay calm even if you can't come up with a great answer or complete the task at hand.

Most people might think that the interview starts once the interviewer asks the first question. Truthfully, it starts the night before, the moment you have any sort of interaction with anyone associated with the residency program. For most, this will be at the preinterview dinner, which is meant to be an optional informal occasion where residents and applicants can meet and where questions can be answered. Sometimes attendings will be present too. Some of the residents and faculty at the function will be the same ones conducting interviews and making the rank list. That is why it is imperative to make your best first impression. If an applicant makes awkward comments at the dinner, residents will probably remember this, which will affect the student's chances of being matched to that program.

Despite the importance of first impressions, the preinterview dinner is also a social occasion. Attire is usually business casual. While it is hard to know exactly what to wear, you can never go wrong by wearing more formal clothes. The worst-case scenario is that you'll be slightly overdressed, which is much more desirable than being accidentally underdressed. You can show up at these functions a few minutes late, as only a small percentage of residents and applicants will be there precisely at the start time. The preinterview dinner is a great chance to get to know the residents and obtain information about the residency program. And while asking questions is good, asking question after question after question can become monotonous and lead to boring conversations. Talking about nonmedical topics every once in a while is a great way to get to know someone. Remember not to talk exclusively to other applicants, despite the fact that this is easier. Most applicants have a lot in common with each other because they are all doing the same thing—interviewing and traveling—and while nothing is wrong with talking with the other applicants, the main goal should be to get to know the residents.

Another important facet of preinterview dinners is that most of them provide alcohol at zero cost to the applicant. This can set up a tricky situation. Having a couple of drinks is socially acceptable, while drinking too much will reflect badly on you. Nurse one to two drinks over the course of the night—being social enough without getting drunk. If you truly do not want to drink, then at least grab a soda as almost everyone else will have some sort of drink in his or her hand.

In the end, the preinterview dinner can be a good opportunity to gain information. Try to make every preinterview dinner you can, though if you're unable to attend because of your schedule, programs will understand.

Most interview days start at around 8:00 a.m., but it is not uncommon to have an interview day start as early as 6:30 or as late as 10:00 a.m. About half the day is usually set aside for interviews and waiting for interviews, and the rest is spent on the presentation, tour, and lunch. The interviews are in the morning or afternoon, and the day often concludes sometime in the early afternoon. If you have travel plans that require you to leave the interview day a little early, it's a good idea to contact the program coordinator and ask to be interviewed earlier in the day. Make sure you do this in advance, as some coordinators will find it extremely annoying to shuffle the interview schedule around on the interview day.

On interview day, wear nice, conservative clothes, be well groomed, bring a pen, and give yourself plenty of time to travel to and find the interview lobby. While hospitals usually aren't that hard to find, parking can be difficult, and finding the room where you're supposed to be can take a while. Arriving late, barring travel disaster, will reflect poorly on you. You risk looking uninterested in the program or unreliable. A few minutes of lost sleep on one day is preferable to being late to an interview. Also, be on your best behavior from the second you enter the building until the second you leave. An overheard careless comment could have negative consequences for you without your even realizing it. It is better not to risk this behavior.

The Interview

As far as the actual interview is concerned, many students wonder how they should act. Think about why these programs conduct interviews in the first place. Why don't residency programs simply rank applicants by their Step 1 score or research quality, or an algorithm that rates every aspect of the application? That way, residency programs could just run everything through a computer and create their rank lists. The reason they don't do this is because a student with a great application might be precisely the wrong fit for their program. He might be too intense or not intense enough. Maybe she doesn't possess the qualities that would make her a good person to work with. Programs have to live with their choices for years, and a bad resident is like a thorn in a program's foot.

Residency programs want to know as much as possible about each applicant, and many intangibles can't be described on paper alone. The programs want to get to know their applicants on a personal level, and this means you should try to be yourself because you won't be able to guess precisely what the program is looking for and what the best response to any question might be. Guessing what the interviewers want to hear and then making answers up accordingly is a bad strategy. Acting fake and insincere will seem fake and insincere. Answering questions honestly and truthfully will seem honest and truthful. Ultimately, your goal should be to be matched with the program that is the best fit for you. When a program is a great fit for an applicant, the applicant is usually a great fit for the program. Being yourself will make it easier for the right program to find you.

Of course, a few behavior modifications can help you succeed and avoid looking bad. First and foremost, avoid any unprofessional behavior or comments. For example, do not tell the interviewers inappropriate jokes or make disparaging remarks about the program. In fact, it is a bad idea to make disparaging remarks about any program since the interviewers will wonder whether you will bad-mouth their program in the same way once you leave. Talking badly about other applicants is also a bad practice. Stepping on other people to get where you want to go will make you seem cutthroat and malicious. The truth is that no one wants to work around someone with those qualities, and that includes residency programs. Try to avoid discussing any debatable topics regarding politics or religion as these topics usually rile people. Discussing religion or politics can quickly put you at odds with the interviewer. Of course, if the interviewer asks a question about religion or politics, you'll have to answer, but otherwise, avoid these topics.

You want to appear confident without being cocky. Residency programs want residents who are confident in what they do and know rather than those who aren't. At the same time, no one wants to work with someone who is cocky. Confidence is not a problem for most medical students—most have been on top of the academic heap throughout their lives and are used to working hard, succeeding, and reaching their goals. This breeds confidence. That said, many students are nervous when they interview, which can project a lack of confidence. First, keep in mind that you need to know your application like the back of your hand and be ready to talk intelligently and passionately about it. Make sure there isn't one aspect of your application that you're not ready to talk about. This will help you answer confidently. Second, remember that the institution would not interview anyone whom it would not possibly accept, and by giving you an interview, the institution is basically saying, "You are qualified enough to come here, and we are serious about you." Knowing this should give you confidence in your application and in yourself.

Learning about the Program

Apart from doing well on the actual interviews, you should also try to learn as much information about the program as possible. Getting a good feel for a program in one day is hard, and figuring out where to rank a program can be even harder. Know what aspects of a residency program you're looking for and what questions to ask (see chapter 10, "The Fourth Year in a Nutshell"), but suffice it to say here that while the program is interviewing the applicant, the applicant should be interviewing the program. Residency programs will almost always portray themselves in a positive light on interview days, and the information they offer you may be biased and not entirely true. There are two solutions to this problem. The first is to go back to the institution after your interview day and spend a couple of days rotating there—that is, take a second look. Some programs look favorably on applicants who come back for a second look as it demonstrates their seriousness about the program. This could even move you up the rank list. (Programs are not supposed to require students to do a second look for ranking purposes.) Alas, this is usually impractical. You might have no free time or money after the interview season, so reserve this plan only if you are having trouble choosing between two programs for the top position on your rank list. Most fourth-year medical students do not end up taking second looks.

The second and more practical solution is to ask a student who rotated there. On most interview days you'll meet some students who have either rotated at the program in question or are home students. These students can oftentimes be a valuable source of information. They can answer the questions you're afraid of asking the residents, such as, How many hours do the residents really work? Are the residents happy here? Most rotators will tell the truth, but be sure the rotator you ask isn't a glutton for punishment who never admits to overworking or being unhappy. Ask rotators about the program when they are out of earshot of any residents or attendings.

Contact with residency programs after interviewing is supposed to have no influence on your position on the program's rank list. It is also heavily discouraged by the NBME. However, some programs will contact applicants and some applicants will contact programs. In such cases, applicants should take everything a program says about them with a giant grain of salt because it is almost impossible to know how sincere it is. For example, a program might tell every applicant, "We would love to have you here." Do not be coaxed into telling a program where it stands on your rank list. That is private information. However, telling your number one program it is your top program is fine if it's true. Be aware that program directors often talk with each other, and if two places found out that a student "ranked" both of them number one, that student would lose credibility. Sending a thank-you note after an interview is harmless and probably superfluous. It is doubtful a program would move a student up its rank list just because of a nice thank-you note. I never wrote thank-you notes or had postinterview contact with the program I ended up being matched to.

Summary

Residency interviews are usually the last important hurdle that a medical student must jump over. An important initial step to interview success is to properly schedule your fourth-year free time during interview season to minimize any potential time conflicts. Also, respond to the interview invitation as soon as possible, and try to schedule your initial interview dates on the outskirts of interview season to leave room for future offers. Using discount websites for booking hotels and rental cars will help keep costs down if you don't know anyone you can stay with in the area or you don't have a car.

To achieve success during the interviews make sure you do the following: know your ERAS application in great detail, formulate answers to possible interview questions ahead of time, be professional at all times, try and make the preinterview dinner, learn about the program as much as possible, give yourself plenty of time to get there, and most importantly be yourself and be confident.

In the end, try to find the program where you think you will be happiest. To be accredited, every residency program has to meet certain requirements, which means you should get a good education wherever you go. A truly motivated individual will succeed no matter what. An older vascular surgeon once told me that the best vascular surgeon he ever knew operated mostly on animals during his residency. Residency is not the be all or end all of a medical career. Rather, it is a starting point from which you can and will learn and grow.

Conclusion

Some days it can be hard to view medical school as anything but a means to an end. You might find this to be especially true when you have a large test looming or are in the middle of a draining, time-consuming clinical rotation. During some of my more difficult times, I would literally count down the days until a test was over or I was on to the next rotation. The more trying times in medical school combined with the fact that residency is supposed to be even harder can make the whole education process seem like nothing but a series of steppingstones.

While medical school is definitely a means to an end, it is really so much more. You will enter with an understanding of basic science and no doubt leave with an immense foundation of medical knowledge and skills to match. But medical school isn't just a bunch of facts and concepts to be downloaded into your brain, it is also a journey of experiences and emotions. This medical journey that you will soon embark upon will be unique and will change your outlook on life. So rather than view medical school as just another obstacle in your way, view it as an opportunity to experience life and change yourself for the better.

Remember, the hardest part of medical school is getting in, which you have already done! Whenever I found myself struggling to make it through the week, I would simply remind myself how fortunate I was to have gotten into medical school and to be allowed to become a doctor. If you ever find yourself in a similar situation, you might find some solace in doing the same.

Index

A

anatomy, learning, 62–63
anxiety. *See also* study anxiety; worrying
  counters to, 69–70
  match day, 158–160, 176
  on new rotations, 184
  new students', 1–3
  possibility and effects of eliminating, 70–71
  posttest, 71–72
  pretest, 139–141, 146–147
  procrastination and, 68–77
  rising level of, 80
  study schedules for avoiding, 78
  through testing cycle, 75–77
  test-related, 68–69, 81–83, 85, 89, 91–92
  USMLE, before and during, 97–98
  when entering third year, 106
apartment rental example, 129–132
appearance/grooming, 153, 197, 211, 213
applying for away rotations. *See* away rotations
applying for residency. *See* residency applications
attendings
  at away rotations, 184
  grading and evaluation by, 129–135
  letters of recommendation from, 167–169, 170–171
away rotations, 162–164, 165. *See also* rotations (clerkships)
  applying for, 194–195
  being liked, 197–199
  choosing, 190–195

away rotations (*continued*)
  deciding to do/not do, 189–190
  doing well in, 195–199
  getting information on, 192–193
  how many to do, 191–192
  importance of, 199–200
  malignant programs, 193
  mental and physical effects of, 188–189
  pros and cons of, 186–189
  undesirable personality traits on, 198–199
  vignette, 179–185
  Visiting Student Application Service (VSAS), 194–195
  where to do, 192
  working hard, 196–197

B

behavior
  after interviews, 217–218
  during interviews, 215–216
  at preinterview dinners, 213–214
  professional, 127
boards, studying for. *See* USMLE Step 1 (second-year medical students)
book selection for studying, 121–122, 123, 146
bright students, 26–27, 29
burnout, 42–43, 93, 137, 145, 164, 191

C

cardiology example, 13
caring about subject matter, 33–34
clerkships. *See* rotations (clerkships)

clinical exams as grade component,
115–117
clinical experience, 103, 120
clinical knowledge test. *See* USMLE Step
2 CK (clinical knowledge)
clinical skills test. *See* USMLE Step 2 CS
(clinical skills)
competition
for residency programs, 170
among students, 26
computer applications
diagnostic, 14
grade entry by, 127
interview tracking, 210
making rank lists, 215
residency matching, 173–175
studying/reviewing, 94
test taking, 141
time management, 210
concentration, factors in ability for,
40–41
conceptual learning, 5–15
aortic stenosis example, 9–12
complicated concepts, 38
Einstein's special relativity concept
example, 38
focus on, 3
games for illustrating, 6–11
human metabolism example, 13
reasons for/benefit of, 5–6, 18
understanding versus memorizing, 13
confidence, 71, 216
healthy, 83–84, 85, 86, 87, 88
overconfidence, 81–83, 85, 86–87
underconfidence, 82, 83, 85, 86, 87
worrying and level of, 80–81
in your study schedule, 97
costs
application fees, 169
away rotations, 187, 191, 194
interviewing, 164, 202, 208, 211
keeping down, 218
preinterview dinners, 214
question banks, 146
during residency, 211
of taking tests, 149, 152, 153
courses. *See* elective courses; lectures

cramming
case against, 47
crammers versus noncrammers,
38–39, 42, 46
definition, 35
long-term retention and, 36
noncrammers, 42–47
as study method, 29
by third-year students, 124
types of students and reasons for,
25–31
while tired, 46
curiosity, intellectual, 34

D
details
determining important, 17–18
forgetting, 34
importance of learning, 39
reviewing, 47
types/categories of, 15–18
diagnostic methods, 14
diminishing returns principle, 18, 32
analogy for, 56
gaining points example, 57–59
high-yield material and, 53–61
Krebs cycle example, 49–51
learning anatomy example, 62–63
study time and test scores under, 51
test grade versus study hours, 60–61
doctors, stages of learning for, 32–33

E
efficient/inefficient studying, 37–42,
60–61
conceptual learning, 37–38
cramming versus noncramming, 37
inefficient studying vignette, 19–25
studying in state of anxiety/
procrastination, 71
in third year, 123–124
Einstein's special relativity concept
example, 38
elective courses, 142, 157, 165, 188,
190–192
Electronic Residency Application Service
(ERAS), 142, 163, 166, 167, 171

enthusiasm/passion
  maintaining, 135–137
  showing, 134–135
ERAS (Electronic Residency Application
    Service), 142, 163, 166, 167, 171
evaluations
  at end of rotations, 129
  of rotations (clerkships), 126
exhaustion cycle, 23–25. *See also* sleep
    issues
  of crammers, 42–43
  cramming while exhausted, 41
  importance of rest, 41–42
expectations, 80
  of medical team members, 128–129
  realistic, 89

F
failure, fear of, 71–76, 84
fears, irrational, 84
first-year students
  first-day vignette, 1–3
  learning anatomy, 62–63
  studying (*see* study methods)
flash cards, 94–95
fourth-year students. *See also* residency
    applications
  choosing/scheduling rotations, 161–
    162, 162–165
  creating your schedule, 164–165
  first days and match day vignette,
    157–160
  motivation to study, 142
  program selection, 169, 171–173
  rotations (*see* away rotations)
  taking required courses, 164
  taking USMLE Step 2 CK, 141–142
  uniqueness of fourth year, 160–162,
    177–178
  when to take the USMLE Step 2s, 164

G
goals
  of away rotations, 195
  setting reasonable, 80–81

grades. *See also* test scores
  anxiety while waiting for, 72–73
  categories of, 125–126
  earning better, 137
  emphasis on, 25–26
  factoring in test scores, 119
  real estate example, 129–132
  study hours related to, 51–53, 58–61
  studying habits and, 32
  subjective grading, 125–135, 137–138
  test, 32
  for third-year students/rotations,
    114–120
  USMLE Step 2 CS, 151
grading rubrics, 115, 116, 125–126, 130
grooming/appearance, 153, 197, 211, 213

H
happiness levels, in third year, 103–105
hardworking students, 27–28, 29
healthy confidence, 83–84, 85, 86, 87, 88
high-yield material, 53–61
  definition, 51
  test grade versus study hours
    examples, 54–56
honesty, 134

I
inefficient studying. *See* efficient/
    inefficient studying
information. *See also* details
  absorbing new, 44–45
  processing of, 46
information overload, 3, 4
intellectual curiosity, 34
interviews
  for away rotations, 186–187
  costs, 164, 202, 208
  for residency programs (*see* residency
    interviews)

K
knowledge, useful/useless, 33–34
Krebs cycle examples, 13, 49–51

L

learning
  conceptual, 3, 5–15
  difficult/complex concepts, 38–39
  environmental factors in, 40
  before the lecture, 44–45
  stages of, 33
lectures. *See also* elective courses
  architecture of, 4
  bad, 45
  during clerkships, 121
  keeping up with, 44
  learning before, 44–45
  note taking, 45–46
  professor's research findings in, 16
  recorded, 46
lecture slides, aortic stenosis, 9
letters of recommendation, 167–169,
    170–171
logs, patient, 117
long-term retention of information
  of crammers versus noncrammers,
    36–37
  cramming and, 25–31, 47
  factors in, 32–37
  of simple facts, 39
lying, 134

M

malignant residency programs, 193
matching (residency programs)
  match day anxiety, 158–160, 176–177
  National Resident Matching Program
    (NRMP), 173–175, 176
  ranking of applicants, 174–175
  unmatched applicants, 174
MCAT (Medical College Admission
    Test), 28, 30, 170–171
medical books, 121–122, 123
medical school
  acceptance to, 28–31
  curricula of, 120
  first-day vignette, 1–3
  the journey of, 219
  undergraduate study compared to, 3

medical students. *See also* premedical
    students
  anxiety of new students, 1–3
  bright, 26–27, 29
  code of, 111
  competition among, 26, 170
  first-year (*see* first-year students)
  fourth-year (*see* fourth-year students)
  hardworking, 27–28, 29
  mistakes of, 129
  second-year (*see* second-year students)
  tests (*see* USMLE [United States
    Medical Licensing Examination];
    and USMLE entries)
  third-year (*see* third-year students)
memory/memorization
  difficulty of, 9
  enhancing your memory, 34–35
  long-term retention, 32–37
  people with ability for, 35
  problems of, 6–7
  repetition for, 35
  simple facts, 39
  thinking versus, 14
  using patterns for, 7–8
  what to memorize, 18
  when to memorize, 13
methods for studying. *See* study methods
microdetails, 15–17, 16–18
  studying all, 56

N

napping, 46
National Board of Medical Examiners
    (NBME), 117, 118, 119, 217
National Resident Matching Program
    (NRMP), 173–175, 176
NBME (National Board of Medical
    Examiners), 117, 118, 119, 217
noncrammers, 36, 42–47. *See also*
    cramming
nonprocrastinators, 71–72, 80. *See also*
    procrastination
note taking during lectures, 45–47
NRMP (National Resident Matching
    Program), 173–175, 176

O

overconfidence, 81–83, 85, 86–87

P

pathophysiology, understanding, 12, 13–14
patient logs, 117
perfection
  anxiety and, 80–81
  trying to achieve, 61
personality traits, 198–199
personal statements, 166
pessimism, 20, 72, 85
posttest anxiety, 73–75, 84–85
practice questions, 122–123
premedical students
  acceptance to medical school by, 27–29
  MCAT score, 28
  types of, 26–28
preparation
  for medical school, 4
  for residency interviews, 212
  for USMLE Step 1 (second-year medical students), 93, 99
pressure/stress, 27
pretest anxiety, 97–98, 139–141, 146–147. *See also* test anxiety
procrastination
  anxiety in procrastination period, 76–77
  avoiding, 89
  definition and reasons for, 77
  how to avoid, 77–78
  mandatory activities and, 79
  nonprocrastinators, 71–72
  pushing back test dates for USMLE, 97
  study anxiety and, 68–77, 74
productivity, 70–71
professional behavior, 127, 198, 215–216
program selection for residency, 169–173

Q

questions for practice, 122–123

R

rabies test question example, 144
rank lists
  away rotators versus nonrotators, 187
  computer ranking for matching to programs, 174–175
  creating your, 173–174, 175–177
  by residency programs, 215
  of your residency program applications, 217–218
real estate vignette, 129–132
reasoning ability, 14–15
recommendation letters, 167–169, 170–171
relationships with attendings and residents, 129–135
renal physiology example, 38–39
repetition, 35
  by noncrammers, 36
  productivity of, 60–61
  quality of, 39–40, 45
residency applications
  away rotations on, 187
  celebration after, 173–175
  elements and issues of, 166–169
  ERAS (Electronic Residency Application Service), 142–143, 163, 166
  influence of USMLE Step 2 CS on, 151
  match day anxiety, 158–160
  National Resident Matching Program (NRMP), 173–175, 176–177
  program selection, 169–173
  rejections and acceptances, 173
  secondary applications, 170–171
  SOAP (Supplemental Offer and Acceptance Program), 174
  taking USMLE Step 2 CK before, 142
  travel issues, 161
  when to send, 171
residency interviews, 166, 170
  acceptance/rejection notifications, 210
  alcohol consumption, 214
  attire/appearance, 211
  contacting the program after, 217
  day of, 214
  how to act/what to say, 215–216

residency interviews (*continued*)
  learning about the program, 216–218
  planning for, 208–214
  preinterview dinners, 201, 213, 214
  preparing answers for questions, 212
  rereading your application, 211–212
  stresses of, 207
  stress interviews, 212–213
  successful, 218
  travel arrangements, 211
  vignette, 201–207
residents
  at away rotations, 184
  grading and evaluation by, 129–135
respect, 197
résumés, 166
retention of information, long-term.
      See long-term retention of
      information
review materials for USMLE, 94–95, 146
rotations (clerkships), 91, 105
  after match day, 177
  choosing/scheduling, 161–162
  common third-year, 105–106
  end-of-rotation tests/scores, 120
  evaluations, 126
  fourth-year, 160–161
  getting a syllabus before, 114
  grading of assignments, 114
  home and away rotations, 162–164,
      165 (*see also* away rotations)
  shelf exams, 114, 117–120, 121, 122,
      124, 125, 145
  studying, 120–123
  subjective component in grading,
      125–135
  tests and grades during, 114–120
  time off for interviewing, 208
  vignette, 109–113
rubrics, grading, 115, 116, 125–126, 130

S

schedules, study. *See* study schedules;
      time management
scores. *See* test scores
secondary applications (residency),
      170–171

second-year students
  study methods, 124
  USMLE Step 1, 92–98
self-confidence. *See* confidence
shelf exams, 117–120, 121, 122, 124, 125,
      145
sleep issues. *See also* exhaustion cycle
  lack of sleep, 19–25
  studying while tired, 46, 96
  before a test, 98
SOAP (Supplemental Offer and
      Acceptance Program), 174
SOAP notes, 110
specialties. *See also* residency
      applications
  choosing, 142
  deciding on, 136–137
  doing away rotations for, 189
  interview seasons for, 209
stages of learning, 33
standardization in grading, 125–126
Step 1. *See* USMLE Step 1 (second-year
      medical students)
Step 2. *See* USMLE Step 2 CK (clinical
      knowledge)
stress interviews, 212–213
stress/pressure, 27
students. *See* medical students
study anxiety
  avoiding, 89
  confidence level and, 80–87
  vignette, 65–68
  procrastination and, 68–77
  studying as counter to, 70
  your study schedule, 47, 77–80
study guides, 47
study habits. *See also* cramming;
      efficient/inefficient studying
  crammers versus noncrammers, 36,
      38–39
  development of, 27
  grades and, 32
  long-term retention, 32–37
  studying while tired, 46
studying concepts. *See* conceptual
      learning

study methods
  determining best, 29–37
  evaluating your, 47
  of first- and second-year students, 124
  high-/low-/average-yield material,
    53–56
  learning anatomy, 62–63
  long-term retention, 35–36
  medical book selection, 121–122
  practice questions, 122–123
  during rotations, 120–123
  third-year students, 115
  unknown topics, 123–124
  USMLE Step 2 CK, 146
study schedules, 47, 77–80
  anxiety and, 81
  creating reasonable, 97
  USMLE Step 1, 93–94, 95–96
  USMLE Step 2, 145
subjective component in grading, 125–
    135, 137–138
success, relationship of anxiety to, 76
Supplemental Offer and Acceptance
    Program (SOAP), 174

T

test anxiety, 68–69, 71–76, 81–83, 85, 89
  pretest, 97–98, 139–141, 146–147
test scores. *See also* grades
  causes of poor, 146
  cramming and, 32, 124
  factors in decreasing, 97
  grades consisting of, 26
  increasing, 51, 56–61, 119–120
  and job applications, 167, 194, 196
  lowering goals for, 71, 80
  MCAT, 28, 30, 170
  perfect, 52, 63, 115
  predicting, 85
  rotation performance, 120
  scaled, 118–119
  shelf exams, 114, 117–120, 121, 122,
    124, 125, 145
  study time and, 96
  USMLE, 141–147, 151, 166

test-taking issues. *See also* diminishing
    returns principle; USMLE
    (United States Medical Licensing
    Examination)
  crammers' approach to test day, 36–37
  fear of failure, 71–76
  grades, 32
  lack of sleep vignette, 22–23
  memorization, 12
  poor test results, 73–75
  studying time for raising scores, 51–52
  test grades versus study hours
    examples, 51–56
  testing cycle, 79–80
  for third-year students, 114–120
  when to take the USMLE, 96–97,
    142–143
third-year students
  common rotations, 105–106
  differences in third year, 103–106
  effective studying, 123–124
  how to approach, 106–107
  patient logs, 117
  responsibilities of, 133–134
  study methods, 120–123
  subjective component in grading of,
    125–135, 137–138
  tests and grades, 114–120
  transitioning vignette, 101–102
time management. *See also* diminishing
    returns principle
  anxiety and, 69
  away rotations and, 188, 190–191
  breakdown of study time, 57
  of crammers, 35, 39
  crammers versus noncrammers, 41
  for fourth-year students, 161–162,
    162–165
  during interview season, 208
  making time for activities, 78–79
  organization during interview season,
    210
  of procrastinators, 70
  studying while sleepy, 46
  study schedules, 47, 77–80
  study time, 32

time management (*continued*)
    test scores related to study time, 53–61
    what to memorize, 18 (*see also*
        conceptual learning)
transcripts, 114

U

underconfidence, 82, 83, 85, 86, 87
undergraduate study
    medical school compared to, 3
    medical versus other majors, 3–4
undesirable personality traits, 198–199
United States Medical Licensing
        Examination. *See* USMLE
        (United States Medical Licensing
        Examination)
unknown topics, 123–124
useless information, 15–16
USMLE (United States Medical
        Licensing Examination), anxiety
        vignette, 91–92
USMLE Step 1 (second-year medical
        students)
    class notes, 95
    compared to Step 2, 143–145, 147
    learning lecture material, 92–93
    preparing for, 93, 99
    review materials for, 94–95
    study schedule, 93–94, 95–96
    taking the test, 97

USMLE Step 2 CK (clinical knowledge)
    content, 141
    strategy for, 147
    study anxiety vignette, 139–141
    studying for, 145–146
    taking the test, 146–147
    when to take, 141–143
USMLE Step 2 CS (clinical skills)
    dress code, 153
    format of, 151
    grading of, 151
    importance of taking, 150–151
    inconveniences of, 152
    issues for nonnative English speakers,
        153
    procedure process, 154–155
    subcomponents of, 151
    vignette, 149–150
    what to bring, 153
    when and where to take, 152–153, 164

V

Visiting Student Application Service
        (VSAS), 194–195
VSAS (Visiting Student Application
        Service), 194–195

W

worrying. *See also* anxiety
    causes of, 80
    over details, 15–18
    about test difficulty, 97

About the Author

Daniel R. Paull, MD, received his medical degree from the University of Miami Leonard M. Miller School of Medicine, where he excelled in his academic studies while still managing to keep a balanced life. He also holds a bachelor of science in physics, which he earned from New York University. Currently he enjoys mentoring medical students through his role as an orthopedic surgery resident at the University of Toledo Medical Center in Toledo, Ohio.

Dr. Paull would love to hear from any prospective or current medical students and can be reached at dan@soyougotintomedicalschool.com.

Made in the USA
Middletown, DE
26 June 2015